VOL **13** MET-NER
1055–1142

FUNK & WAGNALLS **new**
ENCYCLOPEDIA
OF SCIENCE

FUNK & WAGNALLS, INC.

HOW TO USE FUNK & WAGNALLS NEW ENCYCLOPEDIA OF SCIENCE

Volumes 1 through 21 have information printed on the front covers, spine, and title pages that make it easy to find the articles you want to read.

- Volume numbers are printed in all three places in Volumes 1 through 21.
- Letter breaks — $\frac{COL}{DIA}$ — are printed in all three places in Volumes 1 through 21. The letters above the line are the first three letters of the first article title in the volume. The letters below the line are the first three letters of the last article title in the volume.
- Page breaks — $\frac{351}{438}$ — are printed on the spines and title pages of Volumes 1 through 21. They provide the page numbers of the first and last text pages in the volume.

Articles are arranged alphabetically by title in Volumes 1 through 21. Most titles are printed in **BOLD-FACE CAPITAL** letters. Some titles are printed in even larger letters.

- Some titles are not article titles, but refer you to the actual article title. Within articles you will find *See* or *See also* other article names for further information. All of these references to other articles are called cross-references.
- Most article titles are followed by a phonetic pronunciation. Use the Pronunciation Guide on page vi of Volume 1 to learn the correct pronunciation of the article title.
- At the end of most articles are two sets of initials. The first set identifies the person who wrote the article. The second set identifies the special consultant who checked the article for accuracy. All of these people are listed by their initials and full names and position on pages v and vi of Volume 1.
- ◼ This symbol at the end of an article indicates that there is a project based on the subject of the article in the Projects, Bibliography & Index volume. The project is found under its article title, and all of the project article titles are arranged alphabetically on pages 1 through 64 of the Projects, Bibliography & Index volume.

The Projects, Bibliography & Index Volume contains three sections. Each is an essential part of the encyclopedia.

- Projects based on articles in the encyclopedia are found in the first section. Each is both entertaining and educational. Each is designed for use by a student and for parental participation if desired.
- Bibliography reading lists in the second section list books under general scientific categories that are also titles of major articles. Each book listed is marked with either a YA (Young Adult) or J (Juvenile) reading level indicator. YA generally applies to readers at the junior high level or higher. J applies to readers at grade levels below junior high school.
- Index entries for all article titles plus many subjects that are not article titles are found in the third section. Instructions on using the Index are found at the start of the Index section in the Projects, Bibliography & Index volume.

METRONOME (me′ trə nōm′) A metronome is an instrument that beats time for musicians. The most common version consists of a triangular wood box about 20 cm [8 in] high containing an upside-down pendulum. A spring mechanism that winds up with a key makes the pendulum swing back and forth. A movable weight on the pendulum can be adjusted to make the pendulum swing faster or slower. A scale behind the pendulum shows where to place the weight for the desired number of beats per minute. Each time the pendulum swings, it makes a loud clicking sound that the musician listens to. Some metronomes are operated by electricity.

Dietrich Winkel, a Dutch inventor, invented the metronome. Johann Maelzel of Germany patented it in 1816.　　　W.R.P./J.T.

A key-wound metronome. Courtesy Seth Thomas/General Time Corp.

MEYER, ADOLF (1866–1950) Adolf Meyer was a Swiss-American psychiatrist and a founder of the mental hygiene movement. Meyer was born near Zürich and was educated at the universities of Zürich, Paris, London, and Berlin. He settled in the United States in 1892 and was a professor of psychiatry at the medical school of Cornell University in New York City from 1904 to 1909. From 1910 until 1941 Meyer was a professor of psychiatry and director of the psychiatric clinic at Johns Hopkins University. He was the originator of the term *mental hygiene*, and is known for his early efforts to establish psychiatry as a recognized branch of medicine. (*See* PSYCHIATRY.)

MEYER, JULIUS LOTHAR (1830–1895)　Julius Lothar Meyer was a German chemist. He is best known for his work on the periodic classification of the chemical elements. (*See* ELEMENT.) He was born in Varel, and was educated at the universities of Zürich, Wurzburg, Heidelberg, and Königsberg. After 1876 he was a professor of chemistry at the University of Tübingen. In a scientific paper he published in 1870, Meyer presented his discovery of the periodic law, which states that the properties of the elements are periodic functions of their atomic weights. That means that elements with the same sort of properties occur at regular intervals, or periods, when arranged in order of increasing atomic number. This basic law was discovered independently in 1869 by the Russian chemist Dmitri Mendeleev, who received more recognition for the discovery than did Meyer. (*See* MENDELEEV.) *See also* ATOMIC NUMBER; ATOMIC WEIGHT.

MICA (mī′ kə) Mica is the name of a group of rock-forming minerals that contain aluminum, oxygen, silicon, and potassium. Mica has the property of perfect basal cleavage, which means that it splits into very thin, elastic sheets or layers. There are several types of mica. The most important are muscovite, phlogopite, lepidolite, and biotite.

Muscovite is a kind of mica that contains mostly aluminum and potassium. It is named muscovite because it was once used as windowpanes in Moscow. It is transparent in thin sheets, and translucent in thicker blocks. Other names for muscovite are white mica and common mica. It is colored in light shades of yellow, brown, green, or red. Today muscovite is used as an insulation material in electrical appliances.

Phlogopite, which contains potassium, magnesium and aluminum, is transparent in thin sheets and pearly or glassy in thick blocks. It is yellowish-brown, green, or white in color. Like muscovite, phlogopite is used as an insulating material in the manufacture of electrical appliances and components.

Lepidolite, or lithia mica, contains potassium, lithium, and aluminum. It is usually lilac or pink in color. Lepidolite is an important source of lithium.

Biotite is usually found in igneous rock. It contains potassium, magnesium, iron, and aluminum and has a very glossy appearance. Biotite is usually dark green, brown, or black in color, although it is sometimes light yellow.

Scrap mica, obtained as waste material in the manufacture of sheet mica, is used as a lubricant when mixed with oils. It is also used as a fireproofing material.

The main producers of mica are the United States, Brazil, and India. In the United States, most mica is found in North Carolina, New Hampshire, and South Dakota.

An enlarged view of two types of mica (black and colored) set in granite.

MICHELSON, ALBERT ABRAHAM

(1852–1931) Albert Michelson (mī′ kəl sən) was a German-born American physicist. He was brought to the United States as a child and was educated at the U.S. Naval Academy at Annapolis. Among his early experiments was the repetition of the work done by Foucault to check Foucault's results. (*See* FOUCAULT.)

Michelson began work on measuring the speed of light in the late 1870s. In order to learn more about optics to help in his experiments, Michelson traveled to Europe to study at several universities there. In 1880 he invented an instrument called the interferometer. (*See* INTERFEROMETER.) As part of his experimentation on the speed of light, he measured the standard meter in terms of light in 1893. This is how the meter is now measured as a part of the International System of Units. (*See* INTERNATIONAL SYSTEM. *See also* METER-KILOGRAM-SECOND SYSTEM.)

Michelson is best known for his famous experiment, done with Edward Morley, an American chemist, to determine the velocity of the earth through the ether. (*See* VELOCITY.) Ether is the term that was used to describe the substance through which light and heat were thought to be transmitted. It was believed that this substance was both invisible and odorless, and that it filled all the unoccupied space around us. The Michelson-Morley experiment demonstrated that the motion of the earth is not measurable. As a result of their experimentation, they discovered that the speed of light remains the same no matter how fast you are moving. Suppose that someone throws a ball forward on a moving train. He throws at the same speed that he would throw if he were on the ground. From outside, the ball can be seen to be moving at its thrown speed plus the speed of the train. People thought that the speed of light behaves in the same way, that it would travel faster from a moving body. Michelson and Morley showed that this was wrong. Eventually, in

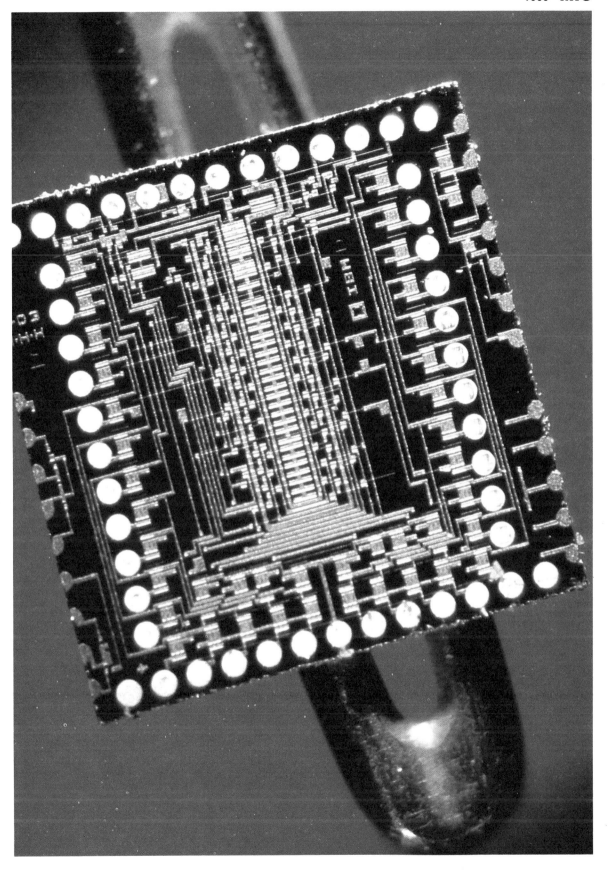

banks, department stores, and schools. Individuals can subscribe to a number of different networks. The terminals are linked by high-speed communication lines which enable users to share data directly. Networks are based on a time-sharing concept in which a number of distant terminals have reasonably quick access to a centralized mainframe computer. Remote users can obtain such information as stock and commodity prices, transportation schedules, weather information, and almost any reference material.

Another modern computer capability is real-time processing, which is the immediate updating of computer files. For example, when a sale occurs in a store, a customer's file and the company's inventory are updated simultaneously through the entry of the sale on a microcomputer terminal.

A microcomputer terminal is the basic device used to communicate with a central computer. It is the data input and output point in a network.

The computer above was built in the mid-1930s. It had 13,000 parts but could not perform nearly as many computations as a modern, advanced hand-held calculator can.

Personal microcomputers   Personal, general-purpose microcomputers can be set on desk tops or tables. They serve two basic functions — computing, or manipulating, numbers and storing, sorting, and rapidly retrieving large amounts of information. Applications for microcomputers can be found in schools, hospitals, libraries, banks, stores, and homes. They can be used as terminals in networks.

Personal microcomputers are designed to be flexible. Software selection and the use of peripheral equipment can adapt a microcomputer to any one of thousands of different applications.

A microprocessor controls all of a microcomputer's activities and performs arithmetic and logic functions. It is located on part of the main system board in the microcomputer.

The microcomputer's memory is measured in bytes, each of which is usually equivalent to one typewritten character. The memory's size is generally described in Ks (one K equals 1,024 bytes).

There are two forms of microcomputer memory. One is ROM (Read Only Memory) and contains internal instructions by which the microcomputer operates. ROM is preprogrammed by the manufacturer and cannot be changed. RAM (Random Access Memory) contains instructions for the particular task that the operator wants the microcomputer to perform. These instructions are entered through any number of inputs, among them the microcomputer's keyboard, a disk, or a cassette. The main system board may also have slots for adaptor cards that provide additional memory or control peripheral hardware.

Peripheral units include input and output equipment, from which information goes to and from the central processing unit. A keyboard is used to send typed messages to the microcomputer. A cathode ray tube (CRT) monitor displays the information that the user is typing and the computer's calculations. A

modem can link microcomputers through telephone lines in order to send or receive information from other computers. A printer produces paper copies of whatever is displayed on the CRT. Disks that are operated by disk drives can store large amounts of information.

To perform a task, a microcomputer must be programmed. The operator may use a program (software) that gives the microcomputer data to process in order to solve a problem. The problem communicated to the microcomputer may be a simple request for stored information, such as a telephone number. Or the problem may be a complex inquiry about a mathematical equation. Program-

mers can write their own programs.

A basic essential of a program is its language. Programming language consists of letters, words, and symbols, along with rules for combining these elements. Some of the program languages are very similar to mathematical language, while others allow programmers to write their instructions in simple, everyday phrases such as ''ADD'' or ''READ.'' The instructions have to be translated into a machine language. Machine language is composed of binary digits that represent operation codes, memory addresses, and various symbols such as plus and minus signs. (*See* BINARY NUMBERS.)

Selection of a language by a programmer depends largely on the kind of job that has to be done and the microcomputer that he is using. COBOL (COmmon Business-Oriented Language) is used to process business data. For complex scientific problems, ALGOL (ALGOrithmic Language) might be used. It is a mathematically oriented programming language. High-level languages which can be used for business, technical, or scientific programming are called FORTRAN (FORmula TRANslation). Another language commony used, especially with personal microcomputers, is BASIC (Beginner's All-purpose Symbolic Instruction Code).

Applications Microcomputers have many uses at home and in business. They can store household information such as income tax records, and they serve as entertainment centers on which to play video games. Stock prices, legal advice, and other data can be obtained. In business, industry, and government, microcomputers handle all kinds of accounting and bookkeeping jobs. Terminals operate at checkout counters in stores, and they help airline employees make reservations quickly by checking hundreds of flights to find available seating.

In the future, the microcomputer will likely have improved memory and auxiliary storage equipment. Their speed may be increased by using very large-scale integrated circuits. *See also* COMPUTER.   S.K.L./G.D.B.

MICROELECTRONICS (mī′ krō i lek′ trän′ iks) Microelectronics is the technique of making very small electronic circuits. A large circuit is made of components (parts) such as resistors and capacitors connected by wires. The circuit can be made smaller by making the components out of very small pieces of metal. These pieces can be connected directly to each other on a flat surface, and no wire is needed. A circuit with many components can be placed on a very small piece of metal. The piece may be only the size of a postage stamp.

Another type of small circuit is called an integrated circuit. (*See* INTEGRATED CIRCUIT.) Integrated circuits were first invented during the 1960s. An integrated circuit uses a very small piece of an element called silicon. A pattern is made on the silicon by etching with chemicals. Impurities are then introduced into the silicon according to the shape of the pattern. By this method, different parts of the silicon become different components.

Microelectronics began with the invention of a device called the transistor after World War II. (*See* TRANSISTOR.) They replaced the older vacuum tubes, which were bulky and fragile. Transistors are much smaller and more sturdy. Microelectronics has enabled very small but complicated electronic equipment to be built. One example is the pocket calculator. Microelectronics is also used in spacecraft. Spacecraft are controlled mainly by computers. These computers are built out of very lightweight integrated circuits. Without these computers modern spaceflight would not be possible. (*See also* CHIP.)   M.E./L.L.R.

MICROFILM (mī′ krə film′) Microfilm is a small photographic film on which reduced images of printed matter and other material are photographed. Microfilm stores a large amount of information in a small space. For example, the contents of an entire book can be photographed, page by page, on a short strip of microfilm 35 mm [1.37 in] wide. The filmstrip can then be wound on a small spool and stored in a fraction of space occupied by a book.

The microfilm copy of the book can be read by putting it in a projection machine that enlarges the image. Some projection machines can make a paper copy of the enlarged image. Most microfilm is black and

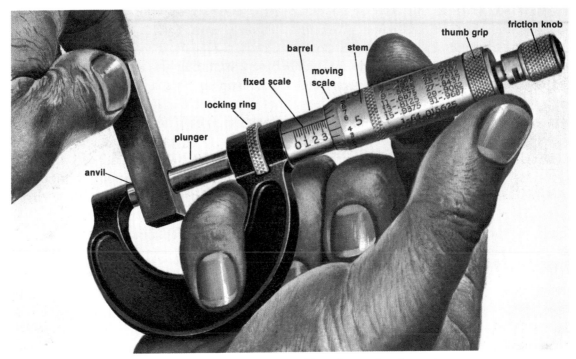

The micrometer shown here can measure accurately to the nearest 0.0025 mm [0.0001 in]. The scale on the right shows decimal equivalents.

white because color is more expensive and usually not necessary.

A microfilm strip that has been cut into short pieces and placed in a plastic card is called a microfiche. A microfiche measures about 10 by 15 cm [4 by 6 in]. Two or three cards can hold a book's contents.

Individual frames from a strip of microfilm can be cut apart and placed in punched cards used by high-speed business machines. The information on the microfilm can then be found quickly by running the cards through a sorting machine.

Microfilm has many uses. Two or three rolls can store four file drawers of business records. A small library can be contained in a few small boxes of microfiches. Newspapers, libraries, and government offices use microfilm extensively. Architects and engineers can store large, detailed drawings on microfilm.

The process of making microfilm copies is called microphotography. It became a large industry in the United States after the Library of Congress began to microfilm books in 1928. W.R.P./R.W.L.

MICROMETER (mī kräm′ ət ər) A micrometer is an instrument for measuring small dimensions. One of the most common types is the micrometer caliper. A micrometer caliper can measure accurately to 0.0025 mm [0.0001 in]. Micrometer calipers are used by machinists and auto mechanics.

Surveyors' instruments have micrometers that measure distances by a screw with a very fine thread. The head of the screw rests against the scale. The surveyor turns the screw to move the instrument up and down the scale. Measuring microscopes often have micrometers attached. Scientists use a type of micrometer to measure the separation between stars on photographic plates. *See also* CALIPER; MEASURING. W.R.P./R.W.L.

MICRON (mī krän′) Micron is a name formerly used for the unit of length now known in SI units as the micrometer (symbol μm). This unit is one millionth of a meter. *See also* INTERNATIONAL SYSTEM. M.E./R.W.L.

MICROORGANISM (mī′ krō ȯr gə niz′ əm) Microorganism is the name given to many types of small organisms. Such small organisms can be seen only with the aid of a microscope. Most microorganisms are single-celled or have only a few cells. They include bacteria, many algae, microscopic kinds of fungi, and the protozoa. Viruses are often included in the list although they are not organisms. (*See* VIRUS.)

A few kinds of microorganisms can cause disease. Such types are called germs. But the majority of this varied group of organisms are harmless. They are necessary for other forms of life. Some microorganisms are used by human beings to make vinegar, cheese, bread, antibiotics, and other useful substances. Vast numbers of bacteria are involved in purifying sewage. (*See* SEWAGE TREATMENT.)

Bacteria and protozoa also form associations with various animals, including humans, by living in their digestive systems and helping to digest food or to make vitamins. (*See* SYMBIOSIS.) But most important of all are the bacteria, protozoa, and fungi which live in countless billions in soil and water. These microorganisms make possible the nitrogen and sulfur cycles and also provide most of the carbon dioxide of the air. *See also* ALGAE; BACTERIA; FUNGUS; PROTOZOA.

J.J.A./E.R.L.

Microorganisms are cultivated in jars of milk in order to provide experimental antibiotics.

MICROPHONE (mī′ krə fōn′) A microphone is a device for changing sound into electrical signals. These signals can then be broadcast through the air or sent over wires to distant points where they can be changed back into sound again. Radio and television stations use microphones to pick up the sounds they want to broadcast. Microphones serve a similar purpose in public address systems and in making the sound portion of motion pictures and phonograph records. A telephone transmitter (the part you speak into) is a simple type of microphone.

Microphones can be divided into two groups, according to how they respond to sound waves. These are: (1) the pressure type, and (2) the velocity type.

The pressure type contains a thin metal piece called a diaphragm stretched like a drumhead inside a rigid frame. The diaphragm is part of an electrical circuit. When the sound waves strike the diaphragm, they make it vibrate. These vibrations produce corresponding electrical signals by changing the electric current that flows through the circuit.

Pressure microphones include the condenser or capacity microphone, the moving coil or dynamic microphone, the crystal microphone, and the carbon microphone. In the condenser microphone, the vibrating diaphragm changes the capacitance of a condenser. (*See* CAPACITOR AND CAPACITANCE.) The moving coil microphone works just opposite to the way a loudspeaker works. (*See* LOUDSPEAKER.) In the crystal microphone, the vibrating diaphragm twists a piezoelectric crystal producing an electric current. A carbon microphone works like a telephone transmitter. (*See* TELEPHONE.)

The velocity type of microphone has a light ribbon of aluminum foil loosely held in a strong magnetic field. Sound waves make the ribbon vibrate. The movement of the ribbon in the magnetic field generates varying amounts of current in the ribbon.

Microphones have been developed for

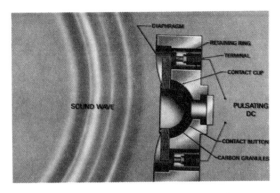

Above, a carbon microphone, which makes an electric current using carbon granules.

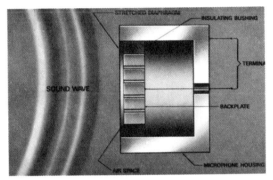

Above, a capacitor microphone, in which a variable capacitance is used.

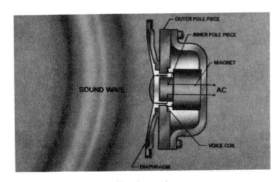

Above, a moving coil microphone.

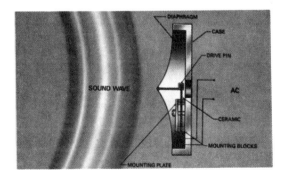

Above, a ceramic microphone.

many uses. Small pencil or studio microphones are used when they will be seen by audiences. Broadcasters and entertainers often wear personal microphones called lavalier or lapel microphones. Wireless microphones have been developed so that entertainers can be free to move about the stage without worrying about tripping over wires.

Nondirectional microphones detect sounds from any direction. Unidirectional microphones are sensitive to sounds from only one direction. A metal arm called a boom may be used to hold one or more microphones over the heads of actors appearing before cameras. The boom can be raised, lowered, or tilted to follow the actors. The microphones will remain out of camera range.

Several people have been credited with the invention of the microphone, including the American inventor Thomas Alva Edison. The first practical microphone, however, was invented in 1878 by David Edward Hughes of the United States. Other inventors who contributed to the invention of the microphone are Emile Berliner, Philip Reis, Francis Blake, and Henry Hunnings.   W.R.P./L.L.R.

MICROSCOPE

A microscope (mī′ krə skōp′) is an instrument used to examine objects that are too small to be seen with the unaided eye. The object is usually called the specimen. A microscope has one or more lenses. These lenses produce an enlarged, or magnified, image of the specimen. (*See* MAGNIFICATION.) If the microscope has one lens, it is called a simple microscope. A hand lens, or "magnifying glass," is a simple microscope. A microscope that has more than one lens is called a compound microscope. A compound microscope can produce a much greater magnification than can a simple microscope. This is because it has more than one lens. A compound microscope can produce an image hundreds or thousands of times larger than the specimen.

The simplest type of compound microscope has two lenses. They are called the objective lens and the eyepiece lens. Light passes through the specimen to the objective lens. In some microscopes, the light is reflected off the specimen. The objective lens produces a magnified image. Usually a microscope has several different objective lenses. Each one gives a different magnification. They are attached to a turret on the microscope. The turret can be turned to bring a different lens into position. The image produced by the objective lens is then magnified by the eyepiece lens. The eyepiece lens can be single or double. If it is double, the eyepiece is called binocular. With a binocular eyepiece, both eyes are used to view the image. The eyepiece produces an inverted image. This means that the image of the specimen is upside down and right-to-left.

In order to examine a specimen, it is first mounted on a glass slide. The slide is then held by clamps on the microscope stage. The slide can be moved about on the stage. This allows different parts of the specimen to be examined. The specimen often needs to be moved by only a very small amount. This is done by using two knobs that are attached to the stage. One knob moves the specimen from side to side. The other moves it back and forth.

Most stages have a hole in the center. The specimen is placed over this hole and light is passed up through it. The light used is often ordinary daylight. Sometimes an electric lamp is used. The light is reflected off a mirror and through a lens called a condenser. The condenser focuses the light onto the specimen. Without the condenser, the image of the specimen would be very dim. The distance of the objective lens from the specimen can be varied. The required distance depends on the magnification produced by the objective. A powerful objective has to be brought very

close to the specimen to be in focus. This is done by two knobs. One knob is used for large movements. It is called the coarse adjustment knob. The other knob is used for small movements. It is called the fine adjustment knob. The fine adjustment knob brings the specimen sharply into focus.

Microscopes can be used to measure specimens. This is done by using a scale engraved on a glass disk. The disk is placed inside the eyepiece. The eyepiece magnifies the scale and it can be used to measure an object. The length of the scale depends on the magnification of the microscope. Its length can be determined by comparing it to another scale engraved on a slide. This slide is placed on the stage and the two scales are compared.

Early microscopes were often ornately decorated. This one has a single objective lens at the end of an adjustable tube. The object can be slid into a holder, just below the tube. There is also a small single lens on the right-hand side for viewing objects under low power.

Preparing the specimen   Different kinds of specimens have to be prepared in different ways before they are examined. Samples of powders and very small grains are immersed in oil. The oil is called the mounting medium. The oil and the specimens are then placed on a glass slide. Samples of pond water containing small animals and plants can be placed directly on the slide. The sample is then covered with another thinner glass slide called a cover slip.

Only very thin specimens can be examined in a microscope. For larger specimens, thin slices have to be cut off. For animal and plant tissue, this is done with a mechanical knife called a microtome. (*See* MICROTOME.) These slices are then mounted on a slide. Sometimes they are stained with chemicals. This shows up various details. For hard substances, such as rocks, these slices are cut with a diamond saw. Diamond is used because it is very hard. The slices are mounted in a plastic or in a hard resinous substance called Canada balsam. The slices are then ground to the required thickness.

A different method is used for metals. The metal surface is made smooth and polished. Light is reflected off the surface and into the microscope. The surface is sometimes stained with chemicals to show its structure.

Magnification The amount of magnification can be increased in a number of different ways. Lenses of shorter focal length can be used. Another method is to immerse the specimen and the lower surface of the objective lens in oil. This increases the amount of detail that can be seen.

Another method is to increase the fre-

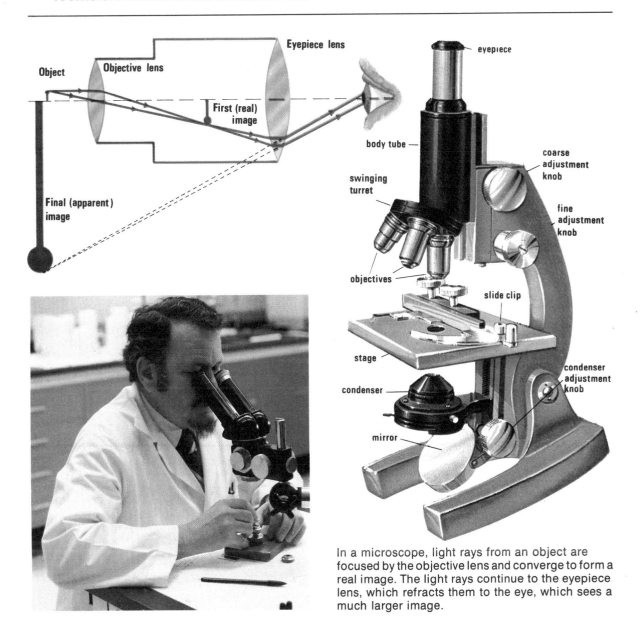

In a microscope, light rays from an object are focused by the objective lens and converge to form a real image. The light rays continue to the eyepiece lens, which refracts them to the eye, which sees a much larger image.

quency of the light used. The frequency of light is the number of times that it vibrates in a second. (*See* FREQUENCY.) Blue light has a higher frequency than red light. For light of a certain frequency, there is a certain maximum magnification that can be reached. At higher magnifications the image becomes fuzzy. The higher the frequency of the light, the greater is the magnification that can be reached. Microscopes sometimes use blue or ultraviolet light. They have a higher frequency than ordinary white light. For even higher magnifications, light is not used. Beams of very small particles called electrons are used instead. These beams can be made with a very high frequency. Microscopes that use beams of electrons are called electron microscopes. (*See* ELECTRON MICROSCOPE.) An electron microscope can examine an object as small as a millionth of a centimeter in size.

M.E./S.S.B.

MICROTOME (mī′ krə tōm′) Biologists often need to prepare very thin slices of animal or plant tissues. To do this, they cut the tissues using a microtome. A microtome is an instrument used to cut materials so thin they can be seen through a microscope. The microtome has a holder in which the specimen is clamped, a razor-sharp knife, and a knife guide. The microtome also has a turnscrew which regulates the thickness of the slice. Wax usually holds the specimen together so the microtome can slice it thin enough for light to pass through. *See also* MICROSCOPE.

J.J.A./E.R.L.

MICROWAVE (mī′ krə wāv′) A microwave is a very short radio wave. It varies in length from 1 mm to 30 cm [0.04 to 12 in]. Microwaves, like light waves, may be reflected and focused (concentrated). But microwaves can pass through rain, smoke, and fog.

Much radar operates with waves in the microwave range. Microwaves are also used in repeater, or relay, systems. Such systems can transmit long distance telephone calls or television programs. In television, microwave transmission sends programs from pickup cameras in the field to the television transmitter. Microwaves transmit pictures and printed matter at tremendous speed in a process called Ultrafax.

Electronic ranges use microwaves roughly 12.5 cm [5 in] in length. These waves penetrate a piece of food and heat the interior by agitation of the molecules. This method cooks much faster than heat applied to the exterior.

In microwave spectroscopy, microwaves are used to study the structure of molecules and crystals. Microwaves are also used in radio astronomy and in nuclear physics research.

J.J.A./L.L.R.

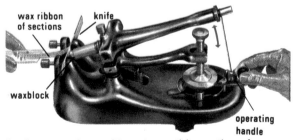

A microtome is used to cut very thin sections from a specimen embedded in wax.

Microwave observations of the earth taken by a satellite over Indiana (left) and Kentucky (right).

MIDNIGHT SUN (mid′ nīt′ sən) The midnight sun occurs in polar regions when the sun appears above the horizon at midnight. Because of the earth's tilt, each hemisphere is inclined toward the sun during its summer and away from the sun during its winter. At the north pole, there is a six month period of daylight between March 21 and September 21. The other six months are spent in continuous darkness.

At the Arctic Circle, the midnight sun occurs on one day, June 21. The number of days of the midnight sun increases north of the Arctic Circle. Extreme northern latitudes are sometimes called the "lands of the midnight sun." *See also* SEASON.   J.M.C./C.R.

The midnight sun shines over a fjord in northern Norway. The sun appears above the horizon at midnight from mid May to the end of July.

MIGRATION (mī grā′ shən) A migration is a regular movement of animals that occurs at the same time and place each year. It is a two-way process. The animals leave an area and return to the same area some time later. Migrations often start before winter. Animals leave an area that is soon to become cold. They go to an area that is warm. Food is available in the warm areas. Some animals that do not migrate must hibernate during the winter because there is not enough food to eat. (*See* HIBERNATION.) Many birds that live in North America from April to September fly to South America during the months of October to March. In this way, they are always living in summer. (Summer occurs in South America during the winter of North America.)

Birds Birds are perhaps the best-known of the migratory animals. Most of the songbirds in North America fly south for the winter. There is a tradition that says that a robin is the first sign of spring. The robin flies south for the winter and when it returns north, spring is soon to arrive. Swallows also migrate long distances. There is a town in California named Capistrano. The swallows come back to this town nearly the same day every spring. Waterfowl, such as geese and ducks, do not always fly all the way to South America. Many of these birds spend the winters in the southern United States and Mexico. In many places the hunting season occurs during the fall migration of ducks. Hawks, eagles, and other birds of prey also migrate south for the winter. (*See* DUCK; GOOSE; ROBIN; SWALLOW.)

Fish Fish also make long migrations. Many salt-water fish travel thousands of kilometers during the year in order to stay in warm waters where there is plenty of food. Tuna swim hundreds of kilometers south for the winter. They swim back north in the spring. Other fish make shorter migrations. Sharks, flounder, and bluefish swim to the deep offshore waters for the winter and return to the shallow coastal waters in the summer.

Some fish migrations are made in order for the fish to reproduce, or spawn. (*See* REPRODUCTION; SPAWNING.) Although most fish spawn in the same type of water in which they usually live, some species migrate to or from the ocean in order to spawn. Species that migrate from the ocean to fresh-water rivers to spawn are called anadromous fish. Salmon are the best known of the anadromous fish. Every spring, these fish swim up the rivers and spawn in fresh water. Most species of salmon die after they spawn. After the young

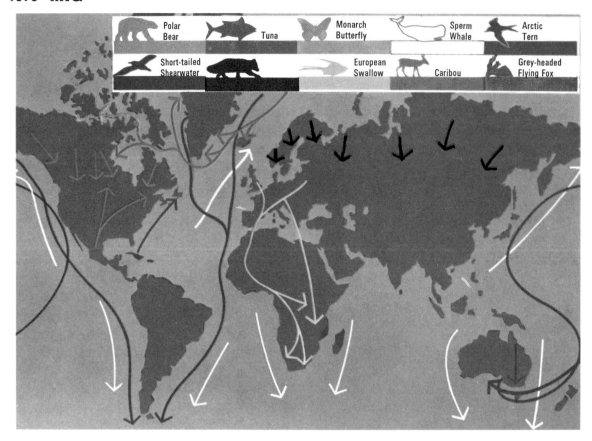

| Polar Bear | Tuna | Monarch Butterfly | Sperm Whale | Arctic Tern |
| Short-tailed Shearwater | | European Swallow | Caribou | Grey-headed Flying Fox |

Above, a map showing the movements of some of the migratory animals of the world, keyed by the colors for each one.

fish hatch, they live in the river for several years before they go to the sea. The salmon live in the sea for two or three years before they swim back to the same river in which they were hatched to spawn.

Species that migrate from fresh water to salt water to spawn are called catadromous fish. The best-known catadromous species is the American eel. During the late spring, the adult eels swim down rivers in which they have lived for many years. Once in the sea, the eels swim to an area in the Atlantic Ocean called the Sargasso Sea. Here they spawn and die. The young eels drift in the sea and after several springs enter rivers. The male eels stay near the mouth of the rivers, but the females go far upstream—sometimes traveling thousands of kilometers. (*See* EEL; SALMON; TUNA.)

Other animals Birds and fish are not the only animals that migrate. Many mammals that live in cold regions, such as the caribou, also migrate. They migrate to low-lying lands that are warmer and have more food than the high-elevation, open, snowy regions. Some flying insects also migrate. The monarch butterfly spends the winter in Mexico and the southern United States. It flies to northern

An arctic tern rests during its long migration.

Wild geese are migratory birds. In the northern hemisphere geese fly north to their breeding grounds in the spring and fly south in the autumn.

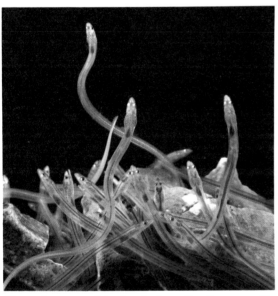

Elvers (young eels) migrate from the Sargasso Sea to the rivers of Europe and the U.S., where they probably spend the rest of their lives.

lands every summer. (*See* BUTTERFLY AND MOTH; CARIBOU.)

Finding the way   Some birds may learn their way from their parents. They make the first migration with the older birds which have made the trip before. These younger birds teach their young the migration route the next year. Some birds may guide themselves by landmarks, such as mountains, lakes, and coastlines. Others may use the sun and stars for guidance. New research shows that birds may be sensitive to the earth's magnetic field. Traces of iron in their brain tissue may somehow act as a natural compass to guide birds to their destination. Salmon and other anadromous fishes may memorize the taste of the water in the river in which they were spawned. When it is time for them to return and spawn, they follow the taste in the water back to its source. Scientists still do not know how all migrating animals find their way.

Other movements   Not all movements are seasonal. Sometimes animals move in or out of an area only once in a while. When animals move out of an area, the movement is called emigration. When animals move into an area, the movement is called immigration. Animals emigrate when an area runs out of food, when there are too many other animals, or when floods and fire chase them out. Animals immigrate to an area when it has something that attracts them, such as food, shelter, and other animals. When animals emigrate and immigrate, they do not always return to the land they left, as do the migrating swallows and salmon.   S.R.G./R.J.B.

MILDEW (mil′ dü′) A mildew is a fungus that grows on plants, cloth, fibers, and leather. (*See* FUNGUS.) It usually looks like a white or yellowish powder. There are two main types of mildew: powdery and downy.

Powdery mildew usually looks like a white blotch on a stem or fruit. It puts out hyphae (threadlike structures) into the surface layer of the host. Powdery mildew can reproduce either sexually or, more commonly, asexually. It reproduces asexually by means of spore-containing organs called conidia. The conidia release spores which are carried by the wind to spread the infection to other plants. Powdery mildew usually does not damage the host severely.

Downy mildew looks like yellow spots on the upper surface of a leaf or fruit. It puts out specialized hyphae called haustoria. These haustoria penetrate deeply into the host to get nutrition for the fungus. Asexual spores may leave a leaf through the stomata. (*See* STOMA.) These spores then produce even tinier spores which float in the dew drops, and can easily be carried by water or rain to other plants, spreading the infection. Downy mildew can cause much damage to a host.

Mildew is most often a problem in damp, tropical climates. It can cause damage, however, wherever there is dampness and poor ventilation. Mildew can be controlled effectively by using the proper fungicide. (*See* FUNGICIDE.) A.J.C./M.H.S.

MILK (milk) Milk is a highly nutritious liquid with which female mammals feed their young. It contains most of the nutrients needed for growth and is, for most mammals, the main source of nutrition for several months after birth.

Milk is 80 to 90% water. It contains proteins, carbohydrates, fats, vitamins, and minerals. The proteins (mostly casein and albumin) supply all of the essential amino acids. (*See* AMINO ACID.) The carbohydrates (mostly lactose or milk sugar) are a good energy source and help the body absorb calcium and phosphorus. The fats are in tiny droplets called globules. The fat globules give milk its flavor, give it a white color, and provide many vitamins. Milk supplies vitamins A, B, C, D, E, K, and niacin. Commercially prepared milk often has vitamin D added to supplement its natural supply. Milk is rich in calcium and phosphorus and also supplies many other important minerals.

Milk is produced in specialized glands called mammary glands. In some primitive mammals, these glands open as pores on the abdomen. (*See* MONOTREME.) These pores

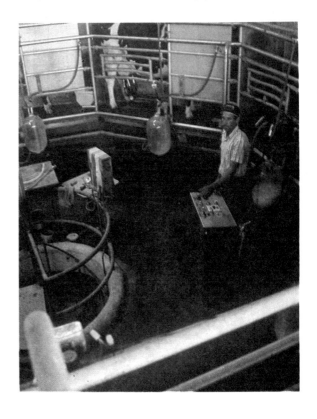

Most milk drunk in the United States is cow's milk. Cows on the dairy farm above are milked by automatic machines in the milking parlor below.

"sweat" milk which is licked from the mother's fur by the young. Most female mammals, however, have structures called teats or nipples from which the young can suck milk. These teats are connected to the mammary glands by a series of tiny ducts.

Most of the milk sold in the United States is cow's milk. In other countries buffaloes, goats, or reindeer supply most of the milk for human use. The content of milk varies from mammal to mammal, but cow's milk is usually about 3.5% fat, 5% lactose, 3.5% protein, 0.7% minerals, and more than 87% water. Milk sold in the United States is usually pasteurized and homogenized. Pasteurized milk has been heated to a temperature that kills most bacteria and other microorganisms. Homogenized milk has been treated under pressure to dissolve fat droplets in the liquid, giving milk a uniform consistency and flavor. If not homogenized, the fat droplets rise to the top of the milk.

Skimmed milk is popular with dieters because most of the fat is skimmed off before the milk is homogenized. Acidophilus milk is skimmed milk with a special bacteria, *Lactobacillus acidophilus*. This milk is sometimes used by people with intestinal disorders. Some people are allergic to milk and are unable to drink it without becoming sick. (*See* ALLERGY.) Other people do not have enough of the enzyme lactase to digest the milk sugar. (*See* ENZYME.) These people must avoid milk or drink specially prepared milk which has the lactose in predigested form. For most people, however, milk and milk products (cheese, butter, yogurt, ice cream) are an important part of a balanced diet. (*See* DIET.) *See also* FOOD; MAMMAL; NUTRITION. A.J.C./J.J.M.

MILKY WAY (mil′ kē wā′) The Milky Way is the star system, or galaxy, that includes the sun, the earth, and the rest of the solar system. The 200 billion stars of the Milky Way spread out from the center in a spirallike fashion. Thus, astronomers refer to the Milky Way galaxy as a spiral galaxy. It is shaped like a flat disk with a bulge in the center. Surrounding the disk is a sphere-shaped halo of faint, older stars and star clusters.

The Milky Way galaxy is so huge that it takes light, moving at 299,792 km [186,282 mi] per second, 100,000 years to get from one end of the galaxy to the other. The sun and solar system are located about 30,000 light-years from the center of the galaxy, in the direction of the constellation Sagittarius.

In addition to its many stars, the galaxy also contains great clouds of gas and dust. (*See* NEBULA.) But the total amount of stars, gas, and dust is less than the total mass that astronomers calculate. This leads them to believe that the galaxy also contains matter in some invisible form, such as a black hole. All the members of the galaxy rotate around the center, in much the same way the earth rotates around the sun. It takes the sun

The Milky Way, when seen from earth, appears to be a flat disk of hazy light, partly obscured by dark nebulae. In fact, the Milky Way is a spiral galaxy, of which we see only the side view. This picture is built up from a series of photographs, taken in quick succession, of different parts of the Milky Way.

225 million years to make one complete trip around the center of the galaxy.

Observers can see a side view of the galaxy from the earth. It appears as a hazy, glowing band. This band, also called the Milky Way, is part of the Milky Way galaxy. *See also* CONSTELLATION; LIGHT-YEAR; STAR.

J.M.C./C.R.

MILLET (mil′ ət) Millet is an important cereal grain which grows in most parts of the world, even where the climate is dry and the soil is poor. About a third of the people in the world rely on millet as their major source of food. Millet is high in carbohydrates, proteins, and fats. It grows to a height of about 1.2 m [4 ft], and has clusters of flowers in a spike or raceme. (*See* INFLORESCENCE.)

Millet seed is round and is usually white, though it may also be yellow, gray, brown, or black. In the United States, millet and millet seed are commonly used as feed for chickens and livestock. In most other countries, however, millet is ground into a flour which is used for cooking. There are several genera (plural of genus) of millet. These include *Panicum* (common and little millet), *Setaria* (Italian millet), and *Pennisetum* (pearl millet). *See also* CEREAL CROP; SORGHUM.

A.J.C./F.W.S.

MILLIBAR (mil′ ə bär′) The millibar is a unit used in meteorology, the study of the weather. (*See* METEOROLOGY.) It is used to measure atmospheric pressure. Pressure is a force exerted over an area. One millibar is the pressure exerted by a force of 100 newtons over an area of one square meter [10.76 sq ft]. It is equivalent to a pressure of 1/32nd of an inch of mercury. Atmospheric pressure is about a thousand millibars. The millibar is often shortened to mb.

M.E./R.W.L.

MILLIKAN, ROBERT ANDREWS (1868–1953) Robert Millikan (mil′ i kən) was an American physicist. He was born in Illinois and taught at the University of Chicago from 1896 to 1921 and then at the California Institute of Technology.

The most important work he did was to measure the charge on the electron. The electron is a very small particle. (*See* ELECTRON.) Scientists knew that the electron has an electric charge. But they did not know the size of the charge. Millikan was the first person to measure it. He won the Nobel Prize for Physics in 1923 for this work.

M.E./D.G.F.

MILLIPEDE (mil′ ə pēd′) A millipede is a tube-shaped arthropod with many legs. The millipede usually lives in dark, damp places, such as leaf litter, or under stones and rotting logs. Millipede means ''a thousand feet.'' But no millipedes have that many feet. Some kinds have as many as 115 pairs of legs. The millipede has a segmented body. Nearly every segment of the body has two pairs of legs. The first three or four segments and the last one or two segments may be without legs. Millipedes vary from 0.3 to 23 cm [0.13 to 9 in] in length. The millipede has a round head. The head bears a pair of short antennae.

Millipedes usually feed on plant material, eating dead and decaying matter most of the time. But sometimes millipedes damage potatoes and other root crops growing in damp soil.

J.J.A./J.E.R.

A millipede on a piece of rotten wood. Its head is on the left of the picture, and one antenna can be seen searching for food.

Flowers of the Bee Orchid (above) and the Fly Orchid (above right) both resemble female insects. This mimicry attracts male insects for pollination.

At first glance this wasp fly looks like a genuine wasp. This excellent form of mimicry serves to stop predators from attacking the fly.

MIMICRY (mim′ i krē) Mimicry is the close imitation of plants and animals by other plants or animals. A harmless species can protect itself by looking like a harmful species. Other animals think the species is dangerous so they leave it alone.

Many dangerous plants and animals have bright colors and patterns. This is called warning coloration. (*See* WARNING COLORATION.) After an animal has eaten several bad-tasting animals, it learns to avoid them. Any other animal that looks like the bad-tasting species is also avoided. The bad-tasting species is called the model. A good-tasting species that resembles the model is called a mimic. In order to escape predation, the mimic must live in the same area as the model. Mimicry is very common in insects. Many snakes also mimic. Some species of king-snakes have the same colors as do the poisonous coral snakes.

Mimicry is not always used just for defense. Some animals mimic harmless animals so that prey will not be afraid of them. The zone-tailed hawk flies as the vulture does. A vulture does not eat living animals, so small animals will come out in the open when it is flying overhead. By imitating the vulture, the zone-tailed hawk can catch these small animals. A praying mantis can look like a stick. Other insects do not see it and go close to the mantis, which then eats them. Some flowers use mimicry to reproduce. The blossom of certain orchids resembles a female insect. This attracts male insects. When the males climb inside the flower, they brush against the pollen and pollinate the flower. (*See* POLLINATION.) S.R.G./R.J.B.

MIMOSA (mə mō′ sə) Mimosa is a genus of about 250 species of herbaceous plants, shrubs, and trees belonging to the pea family. Most are native to tropical Central and South America, though some varieties grow in the temperate regions of North America and Europe. Small flowers grow in clusters as heads or spikes in the axils. (*See* INFLORESCENCE.) The flowers have four or five partially fused petals and may be white, pink, or light purple. They produce seeds in flat pods called legumes. (*See* FRUIT.)

The leaves of the mimosa are small and featherlike. The leaves of some species, such as *Mimosa pudica,* are thigmonastic. This means they respond to touch by drooping. If one leaf is touched, all of the leaves droop. (*See* MOVEMENT OF PLANTS.) This reaction is due to a change in the pressure within the cells of the plant. *See also* PEA FAMILY.

A.J.C./M.H.S.

MINERAL (min′ rəl) Minerals are crystalline elements or compounds of elements that occur naturally in the earth. Rocks are made up of minerals. Most rocks are a mixture of minerals but some rocks contain only one mineral. (*See* ROCK.)

Some minerals contain just one element. These elements are called native elements. They include gold, silver, copper, iron, carbon, and sulfur. However, most minerals are compounds of several elements. The most common elements found in minerals are, in order, oxygen, silicon, aluminum, iron, calcium, sodium, potassium, and magnesium. Geologists have discovered about 2,000 minerals. Of these, only about 100 are common.

Formation of minerals Minerals are formed in many different ways. Magma is molten rock that lies beneath the earth's surface. (*See* MAGMA.) Magma tends to move up to the surface and as it does it cools and solidifies, forming minerals. Many common oxide and silicate minerals are formed in this manner, including quartz, feldspar, and magnetite. Minerals are also formed by the gases given off by magma, especially in volcanoes. These gases cool and condense to form minerals. Sulfur is formed by this method. Many minerals are formed from material dissolved in water. Water in seas and lakes always contains dissolved substances. When the water evaporates, it leaves behind minerals such as gypsum and halite (common table salt).

Identification of minerals The best place to identify a mineral is in the laboratory. However, geologists sometimes need to identify a mineral when they find it. There are a number of simple tests for this.

Color is sometimes an important clue. For example, the mineral azurite is always blue. The color in most minerals, however, can vary greatly.

Streak is the powder produced when a mineral is scratched. It may be a different color from the mineral and so be a useful clue.

Luster is the way that a mineral reflects light. There are different kinds of luster. A brilliant luster is called an adamantine luster. Diamond has this luster. Quartz has a vitreous luster, meaning that it reflects about as much light as glass. Some minerals, such as pyrite and galena, have a metallic luster.

Hardness is a very important guide. There is a scale of hardness. This scale is based on ten values of hardness, from talc (1) up to diamond (10). It is called the Mohs scale after Friedrich Mohs, a German mineralogist. To find the hardness of a mineral, you scratch it against other minerals. Suppose that it scratches gypsum but not calcite. This means that it is harder than gypsum but softer than calcite. Gypsum has hardness 2 and calcite has hardness 3. Therefore the hardness of the mineral is between 2 and 3. (*See* HARDNESS.)

Relative density is often used to identify minerals. It is the weight of the mineral compared to the weight of the same amount of water. A sample of the mineral is weighed in air and then in water. The relative density can be calculated from these two weights. (*See* RELATIVE DENSITY.)

Cleavage is another property of some minerals. When a mineral is struck, it sometimes breaks in certain directions forming flat shiny surfaces. This is called cleavage. For example, mica splits easily into thin sheets. Minerals are usually identified by using a combination of these properties. M.E./R.H.

MINERALOGY (min′ ə räl′ ə jē) Mineralogy is the study of minerals. People who study mineralogy are called mineralogists. They study the physical properties of minerals, such as their hardness. They study the chemical composition of minerals. This means finding out what elements a mineral contains and how much of each element. They also study the structure of minerals, or how the atoms of each element are arranged in a mineral. Other studies include where minerals occur and how they are formed. Mineralogists try to make minerals by repeating the conditions in nature that created them. These conditions may include very high temperatures and pressures.

A very important branch of mineralogy is called optical mineralogy. This subject studies how minerals affect light. If the mineral is transparent, it is possible to measure how it refracts, or bends light, as it passes through the mineral. (*See* REFRACTION.) The refraction of light by a mineral is examined by a special microscope. It is called a petrographic microscope. Minerals may be identified by the different ways in which they refract light. Many minerals are not transparent. These minerals can be identified by seeing how they appear when they reflect light. *See also* MINERAL. M.E./R.H.

MINING

Mining (mī′ ning) is the process of taking mineral substances out of the earth. A mineral substance is nearly any nonliving thing that is found in the earth. Coal, copper, iron, precious stones, oil, and many other materials are mined. Minerals found at the surface of the earth can usually be mined quite easily. But other minerals are buried far beneath the surface. They can be taken out only by digging deep underground. Other mineral substances are found in oceans, lakes, and rivers.

Human beings have mined the earth for thousands of years. As early as 5,000 years ago, the Egyptians opened up copper mines in Arabia. The ancient Romans were among the first people to realize that mining could make a nation rich and powerful. The Romans had iron mines on the island of Elba. The Romans also sent thousands of slaves to work in Spanish copper mines. In the early 1700s, mining began in what is now the United States. French explorers mined lead and zinc in the valley of the Mississippi River. In the middle 1800s, large amounts of coal were dug up in Pennsylvania. During this time, thousands of people moved to California, hoping to find gold. The gold rush led to the discovery of many useful mineral substances throughout the western United States.

When any mineral substance is found in

Above, miners underground use modern machinery to drill holes. In the holes they will place explosives in order to blast through the rock.

an amount large enough to make it worthwhile to be taken out of the earth, it is called ore. A deposit is an accumulation of ore. Some kinds of deposits have special names. A long, branching deposit, surrounded by rock, is called a vein of ore. Gold and silver are sometimes found in veins. A wide, flat deposit is called a bed. Coal is found in beds. Oil and gas deposits occur in bodies called reservoirs.

Locating minerals The first step in mining is to find the minerals. Searching for ore is called prospecting. Prospecting was first done by people who simply wandered around looking for signs of ore. About 150 years ago, geologists (scientists who study the earth) learned how to make maps of the rocks in an area. Miners had observed that certain kinds

of ores were usually in or near certain kinds of rock. With maps to guide them to the proper kinds of rocks, prospectors knew better where they should search for ore. By about 1945, almost all the easy-to-find ore deposits had been located. Mining experts then turned to prospecting with scientific instruments. One such instrument is the seismograph. The seismograph records the speed of shock waves traveling through the earth. The prospector explodes dynamite in holes drilled in the ground. The seismograph records shock waves from the explosion. If ore is in the area of the explosion, the speed of waves passing through the deposit may be different from their speed in the nearby earth.

Above, copper is mined by open pit methods at a mine in Zambia.

Cars on rails carry ore from the rock face in a copper-zinc mine in Canada.

Prospectors may fly instruments over an area which they think contains ore. One of these instruments is a magnetometer. A magnetometer measures changes in the earth's magnetic field. (*See* MAGNETISM.) The magnetic field is slightly different around a deposit of iron, nickel, or cobalt ore. A similar instrument is a gravity meter. This instrument records changes in the strength of the earth's gravity. Changes may indicate the presence of ore deposits. A scintillometer (a device for measuring radiation) is used to locate radioactive ores, such as uranium. Whatever system the modern prospector uses, he must have a good knowledge of geology, mineralogy, and metallurgy, together with a lot of experience.

Methods of mining After the ore has been located, the next step is to dig the ore out of the earth. There are many methods of mining. Which method to use depends on where and how a mineral deposit occurs in the earth and the nature of the minerals in the deposit.

Surface mining methods are used when deposits occur at or near the surface of the earth. Such methods include placer mining, dredging, open pit mining, strip mining, and quarrying.

Placer mining and dredging use water to get gold and platinum from sand and gravel deposits. Placer miners wash gravel into long sloping troughs called sluices. The gold separates from the gravel by gravity. Dredges are used where there are large deposits and a good supply of water. (*See* DREDGING.)

Open pit mining is used to dig valuable minerals from large deposits in hard rock. In this kind of mining, the soil and other kinds of earth (called the overburden) are dug away from the top of the ore deposit. Then large amounts of ore are dug up by large power shovels. Many iron, copper, diamond, phosphate, and gypsum mines are operated as open pits.

Strip mining is used to obtain coal and other minerals that lie flat near the earth's surface. It is mining in an open pit after removal of the earth and rock covering the mineral deposit.

Quarrying is a way in which large blocks of rock are wedged loose or sawed out of a deposit that lies near the surface. Chains and pulleys are used to lift the blocks from the pit. Miners quarry rock materials such as marble, sandstone, limestone, granite, and slate. Gravel and sand are also said to be quarried, even though the process is more like open pit mining.

Underground mining methods are used when the mineral deposit lies deep beneath the surface of the earth. Miners make a wide hole called a shaft. The shaft is driven (dug) straight down beside the ore deposit. Then a horizontal tunnel, often called a crosscut, is dug from the shaft to the ore. Miners work in a cleared area in the ore called a stope. The ore is sent in small cars to the shaft, where it is dumped into a container called a skip hoist. The skip, which is somewhat like an elevator car, is hoisted to the surface and dumped. The miners keep digging a stope, making it longer, as they follow the deposit of the ore. When the stope has passed through the ore, or when the stope becomes too long to work in conveniently, a new one is begun. In underground mining, the miners try to remove only the ore and leave most of the rock that surrounds it. Minerals mined by this method include copper, gold, silver, lead, and zinc.

The waters of the ocean and some large lakes contain huge amounts of mineral elements. These substances are often obtained by pumping the water into plants where it is treated. Pumps move large amounts of sea water through precipitators (separators) so that the minerals can be removed. Magnesium is often obtained by this pumping method. Sulfur, salts, petroleum, and natural gas are also extracted from the earth by various pumping methods.

Today fewer and fewer mineral deposits are found near the surface of the earth. People must go deep underground to find ore. Less of the minerals can be wasted. Also, great care must be taken for the miners' safety. People are trained in colleges and technical schools to become expert in mining processes.

In the future, it may eventually become profitable to mine lumps of metal called manganese nodules from the floor of the ocean.

Beyond our planet, as space travel becomes more economical, the mineral resources of the moon, asteroids, and planets may someday be mined.   J.J.A./R.H.

MINK (mingk) The mink is a small mammal belonging to the weasel family. Minks are found in North America and in the northern parts of Europe and Asia. The animals live near wooded streams, lakes, and marshes. On land or in water minks are swift, agile animals.

The male North American mink (*Mustela vison*) ranges from 36 to 64 cm [14 to 25 in] in length, not including its bushy tail. The female is smaller, weighing about half as much as the male. The European mink (*Mustela lutreola*) is slightly smaller than its American relative.

Minks eat frogs, crayfish, and fish. The mammals also eat birds and rodents such as mice. A litter of 4 to 10 young minks, called kits, is born in the spring. Minks are usually solitary, but the family stays together until late summer or fall. Then the young go to find hunting places of their own.

The mink has a strong, unpleasant odor. Usually, the smell is noticeable only when the mink is angered or frightened. The mink's main enemies include the lynx, bobcat, some types of owls, and people. Trappers kill more minks than all the animals do.

Mink fur ranges from light brown to dark brown. The mink usually has a white patch on the chin and several white spots on the throat and chest.

The beautiful mink furs are often made into costly coats, capes, stoles, and jackets. The color of the fur often determines its value. Minks have been bred to produce fur from white and pale silver to dark brown. Such developed fur is called mutation mink.

J.J.A./J.J.M.

MINNOW (min' ō) A minnow is a freshwater fish that belongs to the minnow family

Cyprinidae. Cyprinidae is the largest family of fish in the world. There are more than 1,500 species of minnows in the world.

Not all minnows are small. The Colorado squawfish, a species of minnow in the western United States, grows to lengths of about 1 m [3 ft]. The carp, which can weigh 22 kg [50 lb], is also a minnow. Most minnows are small, however. They are usually only a few centimeters long. There are so many species of minnows that they are difficult to describe. They have many different sizes, shapes, and colors. Minnows are found in every type of freshwater body.   S.R.G./E.C.M.

MINT FAMILY The mint (mint) family includes about 3,200 species of herbaceous plants and shrubs that grow throughout the world. They have square stems and opposite leaves. The flowers are usually small, two-lipped, and grow in spikes on stems rising above the leaves. (*See* INFLORESCENCE.)

Most herbs used in cooking are members of the mint family. (*See* HERB.) These include sage, thyme, basil, marjoram, and bergamot. Spearmint and peppermint are among the 40 species of fragrant mints in the genus *Mentha*. The leaves and oil from these plants are used in cooking, perfumes, and medicines. Members of the genus *Coleus* are popular as houseplants because of their brilliantly colored leaves.   A.J.C./M.H.S.

Bugle (*Ajuga reptans*) is a British member of the mint family. It flowers from May to July.

MIOCENE EPOCH (mī ə sēn′ ep′ ək) The Miocene epoch began about 26 million years ago and ended 7 million years ago. It is a subdivision of the Tertiary period.

The Miocene epoch saw the formation of the Alps and the Himalayan mountain ranges. By the time of the Miocene, more than half the modern mammal families existed on earth. These included bats, monkeys, dogs, bears, and elephants. Birds such as ducks, eagles, owls, and pheasants were also common.

The evolution of apes underwent important stages during the Miocene epoch. In Europe, fossils of manlike apes have been found in rocks dating to the Miocene. *See also* GEOLOGICAL TIME SCALE; TERTIARY PERIOD.

J.M.C./W.R.S.

MIRAGE (mə räzh′) When light passes from air into glass, it changes direction. This is called refraction. (*See* REFRACTION OF LIGHT.) Light can also be refracted as it passes through air. This happens when it passes into air that has a different density. If the weather is very hot, the air nearest the ground is much warmer than the air above. Warm air has a lower density than cool air. Therefore, on a hot day, the air nearest the ground is much less dense than the air above it. This causes the light to bend as it passes through the air. Because the light is bent, objects seem to be in different places than they actually are. This false image of an object is called a mirage.

A mirage familiar to most people is the shimmer on a hot, dry road. The mirage looks like a pool of water. It is, in fact, an image of the sky. Light from the sky is bent by the hot air and appears to come from the road. Sometimes the opposite effect takes place. Over water, a layer of cold air may lie under a layer of warm air. This causes the light to bend downward. For example, a ship beyond the horizon may appear to be lifted into the sky. In some mirages, distorted images of distant objects are seen.   M.E./J.D.

MIRROR (mir′ ər) Mirrors are used to reflect light. They are usually made by placing a smooth coating of metal onto a glass surface. The metal coating reflects the light. The metal is usually aluminum. Better-quality mirrors use silver since silver reflects more light than aluminum. Mirrors in the home have the metal placed on the back of the glass. This protects the metal coating but the image may not be as sharp. High quality mirrors have the metal coating on the outer surface of the glass. These mirrors are used in some telescopes. Sometimes highly polished metal is used as a mirror, without any glass.

Mirrors obey the law of reflection. (*See* REFLECTION.) A ray of light strikes the mirror and is reflected into our eyes. The ray of light striking the mirror is called the incident ray. The ray that leaves the mirror is called the reflected ray. The law of reflection says that these two rays make the same angle with the mirror's surface.

Mirrors can have flat or curved surfaces. A flat mirror is called a plane mirror. The image seen in a plane mirror is called a virtual image. Although we can see it, it cannot be projected onto a screen. This is because the image appears to be formed behind the mirror. The image in a plane mirror is the right way up. However, the right-hand side of an object becomes the left-hand side in the image and vice versa. The image is always the same size as the object. In curved mirrors the image is a different size.

There are two different types of curved mirror—convex mirrors and concave mirrors. Convex mirrors curve outwards and concave mirrors curve inwards. The image in a convex mirror is always smaller then the object. The image is also upright and virtual, like the image in a plane mirror. Convex mirrors are used as rear-view mirrors in automobiles. They allow the driver to see a large area of the road behind him.

The image in a concave mirror depends on how far the object is from the mirror. If the object is close up to the mirror, its image is virtual and magnified. A magnified image is

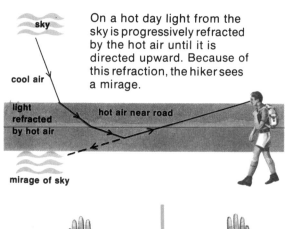

On a hot day light from the sky is progressively refracted by the hot air until it is directed upward. Because of this refraction, the hiker sees a mirage.

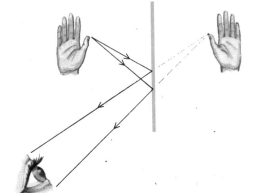

Above, a plane mirror produces a virtual image the same size as the object.

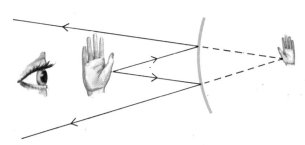

A convex mirror is curved outward. It produces a virtual image that is smaller than the object being reflected.

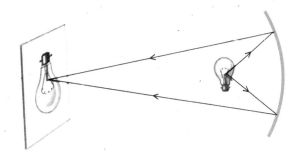

A concave mirror curves inward. It produces real images that are always upside down in the reflection.

larger than the object. (*See* MAGNIFICATION.) Because they can magnify, concave mirrors are used as shaving mirrors. If the object is beyond a certain distance from the mirror, the image changes. It becomes smaller than the object and it is now upside down. The image now lies in front of the mirror. It is said to be real. A real image can be projected onto a screen.   M.E./S.S.B.

MISSILE (mis′ əl) A missile is any kind of weapon that is aimed at an enemy. The earliest missiles were stones. Later, spears and arrows were invented. Today there are many different kinds of missiles. They all carry an explosive charge. They are used on land, at sea, and in the air.

There are two main kinds of modern missile. Guided missiles are guided throughout their flight. Their direction is altered to make sure that they hit the target. Most modern missiles are guided missiles. Ballistic missiles are not guided. They are aimed first and then launched. Once thay are in the air, their direction cannot be altered. Sometimes, however, their warhead has its own maneuvering system which it uses after having been separated from the missile.

The longest-range missiles can travel thousands of kilometers from one continent to another. They are called Intercontinental Ballistic Missiles. This is usually shortened to ICBM. ICBMs go very high up when they travel. At the highest point, they even leave the earth's atmosphere and travel in space for a while. They carry nuclear warheads. These warheads are equivalent to millions of tons of TNT. (*See* NUCLEAR WEAPON.) Often, ICBMs carry a number of warheads. These warheads are released during flight and are aimed at different targets. They are called Multiple Independently Targeted Re-entry Vehicles. This is shortened to MIRV. MIRVs are very difficult to shoot down.

Most modern missiles are propelled by rockets. The rocket contains a fuel and a compound that oxidizes the fuel. (*See* OXIDATION AND REDUCTION.) The fuel is combined with the oxidizer and burned to form gases. These gases give the rocket thrust. They push it forward. The fuel and the oxidizer are together called the propellants. The propellants in a rocket can be either solid or liquid. Liquid propellants give the greatest thrust. But they are more unstable than solid propellants. The rocket has to be loaded with liquid propellant just before firing. A solid propellant can be stored in a rocket for a long time. For this reason, solid fuels are preferred to liquid fuels in missiles. (*See* ROCKET.)

Missiles can have one or more rockets. Small missiles usually have just one rocket. These missiles are often carried by aircraft. Anti-aircraft missiles are larger. They are fired towards aircraft from the ground. They sometimes have boosters attached to the outside of the missile. They increase its acceleration when it is launched. This means that the rocket reaches its top speed quicker. Bigger missiles need more than one rocket because of their weight. These missiles also have to travel further. The rockets in these missiles are connected top to tail. Each rocket is called a stage. The *Minuteman* ICBM has three stages.

A few missiles do not have rockets. They are powered by jet engines. Jet engines draw in air from the atmosphere. The air is combined with a fuel and burned. Therefore, these missiles can only fly inside the atmosphere. (*See* JET PROPULSION.)

There are various methods of launching missiles. Some large missiles such as ICBMs are launched from underground buildings called silos. The missile is propelled from the silo by a large piston. Once the missile is launched, the rocket fires. *Polaris* missiles are fired from submarines. Their rockets have

two stages. The missile is contained in a tube in the submarine. It is launched from the tube by a rocket in the submarine. Once it leaves the water, its own rocket fires. Small rockets can be carried on tanks, or even on jeeps. There are even small missiles that can be carried and launched by one person. These missiles include anti-tank missiles.

A Polaris sea to land missile being launched from a submarine. Left, the nose of the missile breaks through the surface. Center, the rocket engines ignite and create steam beneath the exhaust. Right, the guidance system sets it on course toward the target.

How missiles are guided Many small anti-tank missiles are guided by wire. As the missile travels through the air, it remains attached to a length of wire. The soldier operating the missile sends instructions down the wire to the missile. In this way he can control the missile onto the target.

Wire can only be used for short-range missiles. Many larger missiles have a homing guidance system. These systems enable a missile to detect an object, such as an aircraft. It can then chase the aircraft and destroy it. The missile is said to home in on the aircraft. One method is to have a heat sensor in the nose of the missile. The heat sensor detects heat from the exhaust of the aircraft. This kind of system is called a passive system. Active systems use radar. (*See* RADAR.) The nose of the missile contains instruments to detect and send radar beams. It transmits a radar beam and detects the beam if it bounces back off an object. If it detects the beam, it follows the object and homes in on it. Other missiles just detect radar beams. The radar beams are transmitted either from the ground or from an aircraft. If the beams are deflected by an object, the missile detects the beam. It then homes in on the object.

A more complicated radar system is called radio command system. Two radars are used. One follows the missile and the other follows the object that the missile is chasing. A computer works out the direction for the missile. Instructions are then sent to the missile by a radio. This method is used for destroying enemy aircraft and enemy missiles.

There is one disadvantage in using radar and radio. The signals can be blocked, or "jammed" by an enemy. Long-range missiles such as ICBMs use a different system. They use the inertial guidance system. In this system, the path of the missile is determined beforehand. Early in its flight, the missile is powered. A small computer in the missile corrects its direction. The rocket then burns out and the path of the missile cannot then be altered. (*See* INERTIAL GUIDANCE.)

M.E./J.vP.

American workers are checking the components of a multiple-warhead missile.   © UPI International

MISSISSIPPIAN PERIOD (mis′ ə sip′ ē ən pir′ ē əd) The Mississippian period began about 345 million years ago and ended about 325 million years ago. It is the earlier half of the Carboniferous period. In Europe, the Lower Carboniferous period is equivalent to the Mississippian Period.

During the Mississippian period, most of the United States was covered by a shallow sea. Amphibians appeared and algae, fish, and shelled animals were abundant. Coral reef formation occurred at this time. Deposits of coal, oil, lead, and zinc also formed.

The Mississippian period saw the beginning of the formation of the Appalachian mountains. *See also* CARBONIFEROUS PERIOD; GEOLOGICAL TIME SCALE.   J.M.C./W.R.S.

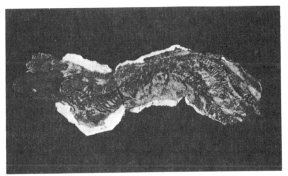

Above, this fossil from the Mississippian period is of an amphibian. During the Mississippian period amphibians became more common than in the Devonian period.

MIST (mist) Mist is very thin fog. When the air temperature drops to the dew point, water vapor condenses into small water droplets. (*See* CONDENSATION.) If the visibility is less than 1 km [3,300 ft] the water droplets are called fog. If the visibility is more than 1 km [3,300 ft] but less than 2 km [6,600 ft], the water droplets are called mist.

In the United States, some people incorrectly refer to a very light rain as mist. A very light rain is called a drizzle. *See also* DEW POINT; FOG.   J.M.C./C.R.

MISTLETOE (mis′ əl tō′) Mistletoe is any of several hundred species of parasitic or semiparasitic plants that grow on the trunks and branches of various trees. (*See* PARASITE.) Although plants from two different families are called mistletoe, most of the familiar species belong to the family Viscaceae. Mistletoe has long, forked branches with opposite, oval leaves. Since the leaves contain chlorophyll, a certain amount of photosynthesis takes place. Mistletoe produces specialized roots called haustoria. (*See* HAUSTORIA.) These haustoria grow into the host tree and take water and nutrients from the

A clump of parasitic mistletoe, which takes its water and minerals from the tree on which it grows, using special roots called haustoria.

tree's xylem and phloem. Since many types of mistletoe get nourishment from both the host plant and from their own photosynthesis, they are often considered semiparasites.

Mistletoe is dioecious, with male flowers growing on some plants and female flowers growing on others. (*See* DIOECIOUS.) The tiny yellow flowers usually grow in compact spikes. (*See* INFLORESCENCE.) These flowers produce small, fleshy, white berries. These berries are a favorite food of birds, but are poisonous to animals and human beings. When a bird eats mistletoe berries, some of the seeds stick to its beak. They are dislodged later when the bird sharpens its beak by scraping it on the bark of a tree. (*See* DISPERSION OF PLANTS.) The seeds often stick to the bark where they begin to germinate. (*See* GERMINATION.) As the seed grows, it puts out haustoria which lodge firmly in the bark.

American mistletoe belongs to the genus *Phoradendron*. European mistletoe belongs to the genus *Viscum*. Dwarf mistletoe belongs to the genus *Arceuthobium*. Mistletoe has been considered a sacred or ceremonial plant in some cultures for centuries.

A.J.C./M.H.S.

MITE (mīt) Mites are small arachnids. They are not insects, but are closely related to ticks, spiders, and scorpions.

Some mites live in water. Others live on land. Some are too small to be seen by the naked eye and must be studied under a microscope. Mites have saclike bodies with a slight dividing line between the abdomen and the combined head and thorax. They have four pairs of legs. The young larvae of most species hatch from eggs and have six legs. Later they shed their skins and change into nymphs with eight legs. After one or more other moltings, the nymphs change into adults.

Most mites live as parasites. They suck the blood of animals or the juice from plants and also eat cell tissues. The mouth has piercing and grasping organs. The mite's digestive system begins in its sucking beak. Several kinds of mites burrow into the skin of people and other mammals, such as horses, cattle, and sheep. They cause the skin to break out and itch, forming scales and mange. The troublesome chiggers, or red bugs, which torment people who have been in the woods or fields are mites. The "red spiders" on house plants are mites, not spiders. *See also* PARASITE; TICK.   W.R.P./J.E.R.

The galls on these leaves are made by some kinds of mites. Unlike most mites, gall mites have only two pairs of legs.

MITOCHONDRIA (mīt′ ə kän′ drē ə) Mitochondria are tiny structures, or organelles, found inside many living cells where food is burned to provide the cell with energy. Mitochondria are the "powerhouses" of animal cells. They are found in both plant and animal cells. A cell can contain as few as one or as many as 1,000 mitochondria. Mitochondria are quite varied in size and shape. Each mitochondrion is enclosed by a membrane and has another membrane folded inside it.

Chemicals derived from food are broken down on the surfaces of this inner membrane by a series of biochemical reactions known as the Krebs cycle. (*See* KREBS CYCLE.) The Krebs cycle uses water, releases water and carbon dioxide as wastes, and enables the formation of adenosine triphosphate by the membrane. (*See* ATP.) This is the form of energy used to power cell processes.

W.R.P./E.R.L.

MITOSIS (mī tō′ səs) Mitosis is the process of cell division in which one parent cell produces two "daughter" cells, each of which is genetically identical to the parent. Mitosis goes on continuously in the bodies of multicellular plants and animals. It is the means of

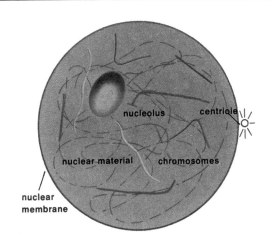

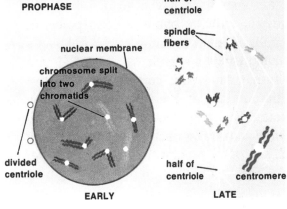

Mitosis is the process of division that occurs in animal and plant cells. In plants stages of mitosis can often be seen in the growing points of the stem and root. Between mitotic divisions the cell and its nucleus rest (Interphase). The chromosomes are long and threadlike and cannot usually be seen under a microscope. During the first stage of mitosis (Prophase) each chromosome divides into two chromatids which are linked by a centromere. The centriole divides outside the nuclear membrane, which then breaks down. The cytoplasm of the cell begins to form a spindle of threads, to which the chromatids attach themselves. The middle stage of mitosis (Metaphase) begins when the chromatids align themselves on a plate and the centromere divides. The chromatids are pulled apart by the spindle and one chromatid from each pair is pulled toward each half of the cell in Anaphase. During the last stage (Telophase) the new chromosomes are surrounded by new nuclear membranes and the cell wall also divides to form two identical cells.

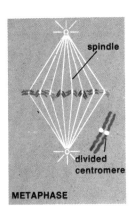

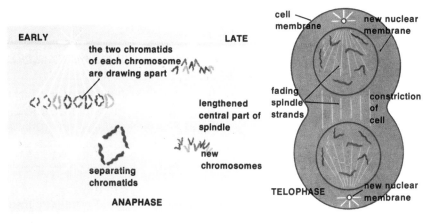

replacing worn-out cells and producing new ones. (*See* GROWTH.) It is a common means of reproduction in one-celled organisms. (*See* ASEXUAL REPRODUCTION.)

There are four stages in mitosis: prophase, metaphase, anaphase, and telophase. These are followed by interphase, a resting and reproductively inactive stage. In early prophase (or late interphase), the chromosomes double, forming two "sister" chromatids which are joined by a centromere. (*See* CHROMOSOME.) The centrioles, rod-shaped bundles located just outside the nucleus, also double at this time. (*See* CELL.) As prophase continues, the nuclear membrane begins to dissolve. The centrioles move to opposite ends (poles) of the cell. Fibers form between the poles in a structure called a spindle.

In metaphase, the chromatid pairs move to the middle of the spindle, called the equator. The centromeres attach to the fibers at the equator with one chromatid resting on each side of the equator. In late metaphase (or early anaphase), the centromeres begin to split.

In anaphase, the centromeres have split and each chromatid becomes a chromosome. The chromosome pairs separate and the spindle fibers begin pulling the chromosomes toward the poles.

In telophase, the new chromosomes are enclosed by new nuclear membranes. The cell itself divides at the equator, forming two new cells, each of which has a full set of chromosomes. Near the end of telophase, the chromosomes elongate and once again become almost invisible. This final stage of mitosis is followed by another interphase.

The entire process of mitosis may take only a few minutes or may last for several hours, depending on the species and the conditions. Although mitosis is basically the same in plants and animals, plant cells do not have centrioles. *See also* DIFFERENTIATION, CELLULAR; HEREDITY; MEIOSIS.

A.J.C./E.R.L.

MIXTURE (miks' chər) A mixture contains two or more different substances that are not bonded together chemically. It is important to understand the difference between a mixture and a compound. In a compound the atoms of a substance are held together by chemical bonds. In a mixture the substances are simply mixed together. For example, salt is a compound of sodium and chlorine atoms bonded together. Salt has properties that are quite different from those of sodium and chlorine. Put some salt crystals in a cup and then add some sugar crystals. Now shake the two together and you will have a mixture. The mixture is both salty and sweet. The mixture has no new properties of its own.

Gases and liquids can also form mixtures. For example, the air we breathe is mostly a mixture of oxygen and nitrogen. Oil and water will also form a mixture if they are shaken together.   M.E./A.I.

MOCKINGBIRD (mäk' ing bərd') Mockingbirds are songbirds that belong to the family Mimidae. The best known of them are common in the United States and Mexico. The mockingbird is about 22.5 cm [9 in] long. It has a long tail, a long, slender bill, white belly, and gray back. It is called a mockingbird because it "mocks" or mimics the voices of other birds and other sounds. The mockingbird commonly sings at night.

S.R.G./L.L.S.

MOCK ORANGE (mäk' ȯr' inj) Mock orange is the name given to several shrubs belonging to genus *Philadelphus* of the saxifrage family. They grow as tall as 6 m [20 ft] and have opposite, simple leaves with toothed margins. (*See* LEAF.) The white flowers may grow alone or in clusters on short stems. The flowers of some species are scented while those of other species are odorless. Members of this genus grow wild in northern temperate areas.

Another plant called mock orange is the

calabazilla (*Cucurbita foetidissima*), a member of the gourd family. It is native to the southwestern United States, and is also called Missouri gourd or wild pumpkin. This plant produces a green and yellow fruit that is shaped like an orange but is inedible. *See also* GOURD FAMILY; SAXIFRAGE FAMILY.

A.J.C./M.H.S.

MODERATOR (mäd' ə rāt' ər) Some radioactive atoms break apart and give off small particles called neutrons. Uranium atoms, for example, do this. (*See* RADIOACTIVITY.) The neutrons can then collide with other atoms and cause them to break apart. This causes a chain reaction. (*See* CHAIN REACTION.) A chain reaction is used to provide power in a nuclear reactor. The rate of the reaction in a nuclear reactor is controlled by a substance called a moderator. The neutrons collide with the atoms in the moderator. This slows them down and makes them less likely to cause uranium atoms to break up. The moderator usually consists of graphite or heavy water. Often the rods containing the uranium fuel are embedded in a mass of moderator material.

M.E./J.T.

MODULATION (mäj' ə lā' shən) Modulation is a technique used in radio and television broadcasting. Microphones and television cameras change sound and color into electric signals. In order to transmit the signals, radio waves called carrier waves are used. The signal varies, or modulates, the carrier wave. This is called modulation.

There are two ways of modulating a carrier wave. They are called amplitude modulation (AM) and frequency modulation (FM). The amplitude of a wave is the strength of the wave. (*See* AMPLITUDE.) In amplitude modulation, the amplitude of the carrier wave is varied by the signal. The frequency of a wave is the number of times that it vibrates in a second. (*See* FREQUENCY.) In frequency modulation, the frequency of the wave is var-

ied by the signal. The amplitude of the wave is not affected. The modulated wave is then transmitted to the radio or television set. The set changes the modulated wave back into an electric signal.

Disturbances in the air, such as electrical storms, can change the amplitude of the carrier wave, causing the signal to appear distorted. However, these disturbances have much less effect on the frequency of the carrier waves. This is why FM is preferred for broadcasting high fidelity music.

M.E./R.W.L.

MOHO (mō' hō') The Moho is the boundary between the earth's crust and the mantle. Moho is short for Mohorovicic discontinuity. The depth of the Moho ranges from about 5 km [3 mi] below the ocean floor to about 48 km [30 mi] beneath the continents.

A project called Mohole was proposed in the 1950s. The objective of the Mohole was to drill a hole to the earth's mantle. Scientists could then gain valuable information about the composition and properties of the Moho and the mantle. The project was suspended in 1964 because of its great expense.

The Moho was discovered by Andrija Mohorovicic in 1909. He determined that the speed of seismic (earthquake) waves changes when they pass from the mantle to the crust. (*See* SEISMOLOGY.) This proved that the mantle rocks are different from the rocks in the earth's crust. *See also* MANTLE.

J.M.C./W.R.S.

MOHS SCALE *See* HARDNESS.

MOLD (mōld) A mold is a type of fungus that sometimes grows on plants, animals, or decaying organic material. (*See* FUNGUS.) Some molds grow on leather, clothing, and bookbindings. A mold does not contain chlorophyll and must rely on its host for nutrition. (*See* PARASITE; SAPROPHYTE.) Molds develop from spores. The spores are produced in sporangia which develop on upright hyphae. (See HYPHA.) When a spore that is floating in the air lands on an appropriate damp surface, it swells, produces hyphae, and grows into a new mold.

Molds are classified by the color of their spores. Blue and green molds belong to the genera *Aspergillus* and *Penicillium*. Black molds belong to the genus *Rhizopus*. White molds belong to the genus *Mucor*.

Molds are often associated with food spoilage. If a mold develops on food, the food should probably be discarded. Some molds, however, are used to give certain cheeses, such as Roquefort, their sharp flavor. Some molds help break down decaying organic matter and are an important link in the food chain. (See FOOD CHAIN.) One type of mold (genus *Penicillium*) is used to produce penicillin. (See ANTIBIOTIC; PENICILLIN.)

A.J.C./M.H.S.

MOLE (mōl) The mole is a thick-bodied mammal belonging to the order Insectivora. Moles live underground. They are fast, almost tireless diggers, spending most of their lives tunneling through the soil. The mole's body is well-suited for such activity. The animal has a long, pointed nose and a wedge-shaped head. The forelegs, which turn outward, work like shovels, scooping through the earth. The mole is nearly blind, but it does not need keen vision in its underground tunnels. Moles do not have external (noticeable) ears, but they hear well. The mole's gray or black fur lies in the direction it is brushed, so the animal can easily move backward or forward along its tunnels.

A mole's home can be noticed by a mound of earth above it. The animal's diggings often spoil gardens and lawns. Many people set traps in the animals' tunnels.

The star-nosed mole (*Condylura cristata*) is found in eastern North America. This species is named from the fringe of flesh feelers around its nose. The European mole (*Talpa europaea*) builds a home with many underground chambers. The Russian desman (*Desmana moschata*) is the largest species of all moles. This mole is about 36 cm [14 in] in length, including the tail. The shrew moles are the smallest species. They are about 13 cm [5 in] in length, including the tail.

J.J.A./J.J.M.

MOLE (UNIT) (mōl) The mole is a unit used to measure the amount of a substance. It is one of the international system of units. (See INTERNATIONAL SYSTEM.) All atoms have an atomic weight. This is the weight of an atom compared to the weight of an atom of carbon. (See ATOMIC WEIGHT.) Atoms combine to form molecules. The total atomic weights of all the atoms in a molecule is called the molecular weight. (See MOLECULAR WEIGHT.) One mole of a substance has a weight equal to its molecular weight in grams. For example, the molecular weight of sodium chloride is 58.5. Therefore one mole of sodium chloride weighs 58.5 g [2.06 oz]. One mole of any substance always contains the same number of atoms. This number is 6.023×10^{23} (10^{23} is 10 followed by 23 zeros). It is known as Avogadro's number. Suppose that one molecule of substance A reacts with one molecule of substance B. Then one mole of substance A reacts with one mole of substance B. In general, simple numbers of moles of different substances react with each other. Moles are used by chemists to measure quantities in chemical reactions.   M.E./R.W.L.

MOLECULAR BIOLOGY (mə lek′ yə lər bī al′ ə jē) Molecular biology is the study of the molecules in cells. A molecule is the smallest unit into which a substance can be divided but still keep the characteristics of the substance. By studying cell molecules, molecular biologists try to understand the structure of the molecules and how they work.

In the twentieth century, the most important research in biology has been done in the

area of molecular biology. This has been largely made possible through new developments and new instruments, such as the electron microscope, the ultracentrifuge, X-ray diffraction, and chemical methods of breaking down molecules. The instruments enable molecular biologists to explore levels of the cell that are not visible with a conventional light microscope.

The light microscope can magnify up to 2,000 times. The electron microscope—using a beam of electrons instead of light rays—can magnify over 400,000 times. The magnified image can be displayed on a TV-like screen or made into a photograph. In 1970 the first pictures of individual atoms were taken by an electron microscope.

Molecular biologists are concerned with

These high-resolution images were made using an electron microscope. The lefthand photograph shows a protein magnified 100,000 times. The two small pictures show individual enzyme molecules from the boxed areas of the large picture. The righthand photograph shows the crystalline structure of a diphtheria toxin. Studying and understanding the structures of molecules helps our understanding of how molecules function in organisms.

many phases of how living organisms operate. For example, they study the behavior of viruses and bacteria. They try to trace how energy moves through cells. Molecular biologists also focus on systems that control metabolism—the changing of food into energy and tissue. Another important area of study is how proteins and nucleic acids work in the body. Nucleic acids carry the genetic information that is necessary for the development of cells in living things.

Much of the growth of molecular biology was due to the discovery of the chemical deoxyribonucleic acid (DNA). DNA contains the genetic code, or information, of life.

It has been known for thousands of years that certain characteristics are passed from parents to offspring. In the early 1900s, scientists found that it was the genes in cells that transmit the characteristics. Then in the 1940s and 1950s, it was discovered that DNA controls the characteristics. It is now known that the total genetic process of a living cell is determined by DNA.

Molecular biologists have discovered that living organisms have different amounts of DNA. More complicated organisms usually have more DNA than simpler ones. For example, a cow has more DNA than a beetle, and a flowering plant has more DNA than moss.

Radiation and certain chemicals can cause mutations, or changes, in an individual cell. Some changes produce chemical advantages in the cell, making it better able to survive in its environment. A mutation may, however, cause a cell to die.

Genetic engineers have used knowledge from molecular biology to help them change certain organisms in order to produce others. Bacteria, for instance, can be changed so that they form human hormones. Also, immunity systems in living organisms can be improved. And plants can be made resistant to disease.

Research in molecular biology has also been valuable to the fields of embryology, physiology, biochemistry, and clinical medicine, as well as to industry. *See also* BIOLOGY; BIOPHYSICS; BIOCHEMISTRY; CELL; GENETICS.

D.A.T/G.D.B.

MOLECULAR WEIGHT (mə lek′ yə lər wāt′) All atoms have an atomic weight. This is the weight of an atom compared to the weight of an atom of carbon. (*See* ATOMIC WEIGHT.) Atoms combine to form molecules.

The total of all the atomic weights of the atoms in the molecule is called the molecular weight of the molecule. For example, glucose is a type of sugar. Its molecule consists of six atoms of carbon, twelve of hydrogen, and six of oxygen. Its formula is $C_6H_{12}O_6$. The atomic weights of carbon, hydrogen, and oxygen are 6, 1, and 16. Therefore the molecular weight of glucose is $(6 \times 12) + (12 \times 1) + (6 \times 16)$. This equals 180.

Several substances do not have molecules. Their atoms are grouped together in a regular arrangement called a lattice. In this case the molecular weight of the substance is worked out from its formula. For example, the atoms in sodium chloride are arranged in a lattice. The lattice contains equal numbers of sodium and chlorine atoms. Therefore its formula is written NaCl. The molecular weight of sodium chloride is then the sum of the atomic weights of sodium and chlorine. The atomic weight of sodium is 23 and the atomic weight of chlorine is 35.5. Therefore the molecular weight of sodium chloride is 23 + 35.5. This equals 58.5.

A knowledge of molecular weights is essential in chemistry. Substances react together in simple proportions. These proportions are related to their molecular weights. (*See* MOLE.)

There are a number of ways of finding out the molecular weight of a substance. One mole of a substance is its molecular weight in grams. If the weight of one mole of a substance can be found out, then its molecular weight is known. For example, one mole of glucose weighs 180 g [6.34 oz]. One mole of sodium chloride weighs 58.5 g [2.06 oz]. For gases one mole of the gas has a volume of 22.4 l [5.9 gal] at 0°C [32°F] and at one atmosphere pressure. The molecular weight can be worked out by measuring the volume of a certain mass of the gas. The temperature and pressure of the gas have to be taken into account as well.

A different method of measuring molecular weight has to be used for solids and liquids. One mole of any substance lowers the freezing point of a liquid in which it is dissolved by a definite amount. It also raises the boiling point of the liquid by a definite amount. A certain amount of the solid or liquid to be measured is dissolved in the liquid. The change in the freezing or boiling point of the liquid is measured. The weight of a mole of the solid or liquid can then be calculated. This gives the molecular weight of the solid or liquid.   M.E./R.W.L.

MOLECULE (mäl′ i kyül′) A molecule is the smallest collection of the atoms in a substance that can exist in a free (isolated) state. (*See* ATOM.) All substances are made up of atoms. In most substances the atoms are grouped together in molecules. If the substance is pure, then all the molecules are identical. Inside the molecule the atoms are held together by chemical bonds. (*See* BOND, CHEMICAL.) These bonds hold the atoms in a particular position in the molecule. Therefore, all molecules have a definite shape. Molecules can vary greatly in size. A molecule of hydrogen, for example, has just two atoms of hydrogen bonded together. Some substances in the body have large molecules. For example, a molecule of DNA contains thousands of atoms.

In a chemical reaction, the molecules change into different molecules. This can be done in different ways. Some atoms in the molecule may be replaced by different atoms. Two or more molecules may combine to form one larger molecule. Or the molecule may be broken up into smaller molecules. If the molecules of a substance change, the substance turns into another substance. For example, molecules of hydrogen and molecules of oxygen combine to form molecules of water. Water is a very different substance from hydrogen or oxygen.

Not all substances consist of molecules. Some are made up of single atoms. For example, the noble gases, such as helium and neon, exist as single atoms. (*See* NOBLE GAS.) This is because their atoms are very unreactive. Other substances consist of atoms in a large regular arrangement called a lattice. Many crystals have this structure. (*See* LATTICE.)

The molecules in a substance are linked together by forces. In a solid these forces are very strong. This gives a solid its strength and shape. In a liquid these forces are weaker. Therefore a liquid has no shape. However the forces in a liquid are strong enough to give it a definite volume. In a gas the forces are very weak indeed. A gas has no definite volume. It fills up as large a space as it can.

M.E./A.D.

MOLLUSCA (mə ləs′ kə) Mollusca is a large phylum of invertebrate animals. (*See* INVERTEBRATE.) There are 45,000 species of mollusks. Only the phylum Arthropoda has more species. (*See* ARTHROPODA.) The bodies of mollusks have a head, stomach, foot, and a mantle, a piece of skin that surrounds the body. These parts are sometimes hard to see in some mollusks because their bodies are not segmented. Many mollusks have a chalky shell produced by the mantle. Bivalves are mollusks which have two shells which open and close around the animal like a book. (*See*

The elaborately decorated creature (above) is a sea slug, a gastropod that is a member of the phylum Mollusca. It is only one of 45,000 species of mollusks.

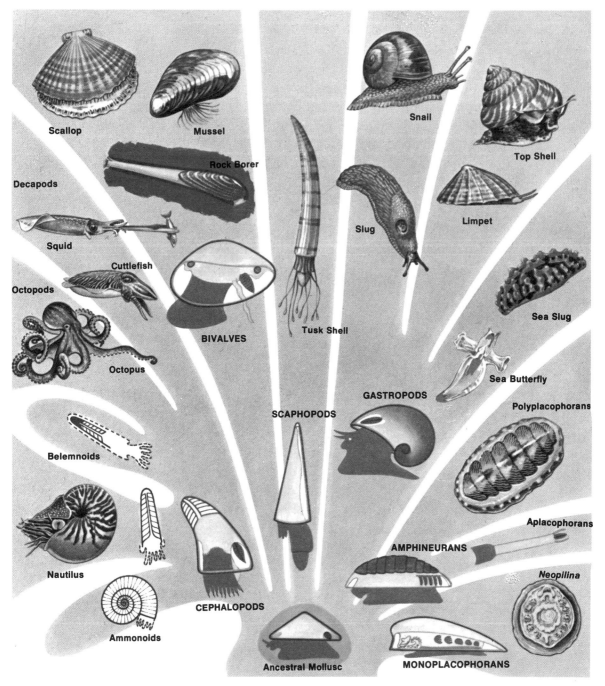

Scallop

Mussel

Decapods

Rock Borer

Squid

Cuttlefish

Octopods

Octopus

Belemnoids

Nautilus

Ammonoids

CEPHALOPODS

BIVALVES

Tusk Shell

SCAPHOPODS

Ancestral Mollusc

Snail

Top Shell

Limpet

Slug

Sea Slug

Sea Butterfly

GASTROPODS

Polyplacophorans

Aplacophorans

AMPHINEURANS

Neopilina

MONOPLACOPHORANS

Six classes of mollusca are shown above. The most primitive living mollusk is *Neopilina*, which has gills instead of a ctenidium as the respiratory organ. The Amphineurans are divided into the chitons (polyplacophorans) and the deep sea Aplacophorans. There are three groups of gastropods. The bivalves have a hinged double shell. The cephalopods are the most diverse class. There are two extinct groups—the Ammonoids and the Belemnoids—and three living groups—the Nautiloids (such as the nautilus), the Octopods, (such as the octopus) and the Decapods.

BIVALVE.) Other mollusks, such as snails, live inside one shell.

Most mollusks live in the sea, but some live in fresh water. Some species even live on land. Mollusks are often eaten by many animals. Man eats some mollusks, such as clams, oysters, and squid. Some well-known members of Mollusca are snails, slugs, clams, octopuses, abalones, and the nautiluses. *See also* ABALONE; ANIMAL KINGDOM; SNAIL.   S.R.G./R.J.B.

MOLTING (mōlt′ ing) Molting is a process by which many animals shed their body covering (exoskeleton, skin, hair, or feathers) and replace it with a new one. Insects and other arthropods have a hard, protective coat called an exoskeleton. (*See* SKELETON.) This exoskeleton does not increase in size, so it must be replaced as the animal grows larger. When the animal is ready to molt, the body releases a special hormone. (*See* HORMONE.) This hormone causes part of the old coat to be reabsorbed by the body. It also causes a new, soft coat to develop under the remains of the old one. The old exoskeleton dries, hardens, and splits. The animal breaks out of the old coat and usually stays in a protected place until the new one has expanded and hardened.

Most scaly reptiles (such as snakes and lizards) molt regularly, each time shedding the outer layers of skin. Most birds molt at least once a year, and some molt three times a year. When a bird molts, it loses it feathers one at a time in a regular order. They are replaced in the same order so that the bird is able to fly during the four to six weeks required for a complete molt. Most birds molt once before mating season and again after the winter. Most mammals molt once in the spring. They lose the heavy, protective coat of hair that developed for the winter. During molting, some mammals replace lost or damaged body parts. Deer, for example, replace their antlers when they molt. *See also* ARTHROPODA; INSECT; METAMORPHOSIS.

A.J.C./E.R.L.

MOLYBDENITE (mə lib′ də nīt′) Molybdenite is the chief ore from which the metal molybdenum is obtained. (*See* MOLYBDENUM.) Molybdenite is a soft, bluish gray mineral similar in appearance to graphite. Chemically, molybdenite is a compound of molybdenum and sulfur. It is found in granites and metamorphosed limestones. Molybdenite is mined in Australia, Canada, Germany, Norway, and the United States.

J.J.A./R.H.

MOLYBDENUM (mə lib′ də nəm) Molybdenum (Mo) is a hard, silvery white metallic element. Its atomic number is 42 and its atomic weight is 95.94. Molybdenum melts at 2,617°C [4,743°F] and boils at 4,612°C [8,334°F]. The relative density of molybdenum is 10.2.

Molybdenum was discovered by a Swedish chemist, Peter Hjelm, in 1781. The most common mineral of molybdenum is molybdenite. This mineral is found in North America, Australia, Germany, and Scandinavia. Molybdenum is used mainly for making very hard steel. Molybdenum steel is used in turbines, aircraft parts, cutting tools, and parts of road and rail vehicles. Like all metals, molybdenum forms salts. (*See* SALTS.) Molybdenum also forms an acid called molybdic acid (H_2MoO_4). Salts of molybdic acid are called molybdates. Sodium molybdate is used in dyeing and for making inks.

M.E./J.R.W.

MOMENT (mō′ mənt) A lever consists of a bar pivoted about a point. The point is called a fulcrum. (*See* MACHINE, SIMPLE.) A seesaw is an example of a lever. It is pivoted about a support in the middle of the seesaw. This support is the fulcrum. If a force acts on the lever, the lever moves around. This turning effect is called the moment of the force. It is also called a torque. (*See* TORQUE.) Weight is a force. If you sit on one end of a seesaw it moves down because of your weight. Your weight produces a moment on the seesaw. The moment of a force is the force multiplied by the distance from it to the fulcrum. This distance has to be at right angles to the direction of the force. The idea of a moment can be applied to other situations. For example, when you open a door you apply a force. The force produces a moment about the hinge of the door. The moment of the force causes the door to turn on its hinge.   M.E./J.T.

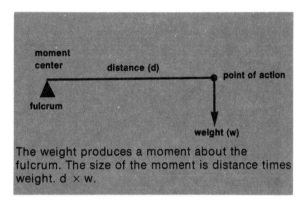

The weight produces a moment about the fulcrum. The size of the moment is distance times weight. d × w.

MOMENTUM (mō ment' əm) A moving object tends to continue moving. It can only be stopped or slowed down by applying a force. This is because all moving bodies have momentum. The greater the momentum of the body, the more difficult it is to stop. The momentum of an object depends upon its mass and its velocity. If the object is moving in a straight line, its momentum is found by multiplying its mass by its velocity. This is called linear momentum. If the object is moving in a circle, then its momentum is called angular momentum.

Suppose that a moving object hits another object that is not moving. The moving object has momentum, but the stationary one does not since it is not moving. After the collision, both objects will move. They both now have momentum. Their combined momentum after the collision must equal the momentum of the moving object before the collision. This is a very important law. It is called the law of conservation of momentum.   M.E./A.I.

MONEL METAL (mō' nel met' əl) Monel Metal is an alloy of nickel and copper. It contains about 66 percent nickel and 31.5 percent copper. The rest is made up of small amounts of iron, aluminum, manganese, carbon, and silicon. Monel Metal looks like nickel. The alloy is stronger than pure nickel. Monel Metal is about as hard as steel. The nickel and copper alloy can be forged and drawn into wire.

Monel Metal resists corrosion from seawater, steam, hot gas, air, or acids. Because of this property Monel Metal is useful in sheet-metal work, in chemical plants, and on ships. Monel Metal is used for pump fittings, propellers, and sometimes as a covering for sinks.   J.J.A./A.D.

MONERA (mə nir' ə) Monera is a group of one-celled organisms that have some characteristics of plants, some characteristics of animals, and many characteristics which are neither plant nor animal. The monerans include bacteria and blue-green algae. In the five-kingdom system of classification, Monera is a separate kingdom. In the less widely used four-kingdom system of classification, the monerans are included with the protozoa in the kingdom Protista. *See also* ALGAE; BACTERIA; PROTISTA.   A.J.C./E.R.L.

MONGOOSE (män' güs') The mongoose is a slender, carnivorous mammal related to the civet and genet. (*See* CIVET.) It belongs to the family Viverridae. There are about 50 species of mongoose, all very much alike, living in Africa and southern Asia.

The common mongoose is about 41 cm [16 in] long, and has stiff, yellowish gray hair that is grizzled with brownish black. It has a fierce disposition but can be tamed.

The mongoose is known for its ability to kill snakes. It also kills rats and mice. The mongoose is not immune to poison, but its swiftness allows it to seize and kill poisonous snakes such as the cobra. The mongoose has been introduced into Hawaii, Puerto Rico, Jamaica, and Cuba to destroy rat populations. The mongoose also kills poultry, wild birds, and other beneficial small animals and eats young birds and birds' eggs.

Mongooses cannot be brought into the

United States without a permit from the Bureau of Sport Fisheries and Wildlife.

W.R.P./J.J.M.

MONITOR LIZARD (män′ ət ər liz′ ərd) The monitor lizards are a group of the largest lizards in the world. They belong to the family Varanidae. Monitors range in length from 1.9 to 2.8 m [6.5 to 10 ft]. They can be as powerful as a small crocodile. The lizards' stocky bodies are covered with rounded scales. Monitors have forked tongues which can be pulled back into a protective sheath in their mouths. The tongue is used to detect odors in the air. Monitor lizards live in the hot parts of Africa, Asia, Australia, and Malaya. Some species live on land while others live near water. They eat fish, amphibians, snakes, eggs, and other small animals.

Monitor lizards are active hunters. They travel long distances in search of food, unlike most other lizards that run short distances to catch their prey. *See also* KOMODO DRAGON; LIZARD.

S.R.G./R.L.L.

MONKEY (məng′ kē) A monkey is any of about 200 species of lively mammals belonging to the highest order of evolutionary development, the primates. (*See* PRIMATE.) Monkeys are usually smaller and more agile than their relatives, the apes. (*See* APE.) Most monkeys have tails, whereas apes do not.

Monkeys live in tropical areas throughout the world. Most live in trees, though some species prefer the savannas (grasslands). Even these land-dwellers usually retreat to the trees at night for protection while sleeping. Monkeys vary greatly in size and appearance.

Three species of Old World monkeys are pictured here with their young. They are (left) Mangabeys, (below left) Guenons, and (below) Colobus monkeys. All three species of these monkeys are found in Africa south of the Sahara Desert.

douroucoulis

uakari

howler monkeys

New World monkeys are distinguished by such features as their prehensile tails and broad noses. These monkeys include douroucoulis, (top left), the only monkeys which are nocturnal. The bald Uakari (top right) is a human-looking New World monkey. Howler monkeys (above left) and squirrel monkeys are other New World monkeys with unusual features.

squirrel monkeys

The smallest, the pygmy marmoset, may be only 12 cm [5 in] long (not including the tail) and weigh less than 90 g [0.2 lb]. (*See* MAR-MOSET.) The largest, the mandrill, may be 120 cm [48 in] long and weigh more than 40 kg [90 lb]. (*See* MANDRILL.)

Monkeys have long arms and legs and are well-suited for life in the trees. Their hands and feet can grasp objects such as branches. Monkeys usually walk on all fours, but may stand or run in an upright position, particularly when holding food in their hands. Monkeys have large, keen eyes that face forward and give both depth and color perception. (*See* EYE AND VISION.) Most monkeys are omnivores, eating plants, insects, and small animals such as frogs and birds. The larger monkeys, such as the baboons, sometimes prey on small, young mammals. (*See* BA-BOON.) A female monkey usually gives birth to one baby a year after a gestation period of four to eight months. She may nurse, protect, and teach her baby for as long as two years. During this time, the young monkey rarely strays far from its mother and often clings to her fur as she moves through the trees.

There are two main groups of monkeys: Old World monkeys and New World monkeys. Old World monkeys are native to Africa and Asia. They all belong to the family Cercopithecidae and include such species as the baboon, mandrill, proboscis monkey, colobus monkey, guenon, langur, and mangabey. Old World monkeys have 32 teeth and close-set nostrils which point downward. They cannot grab onto objects with their tails, but use them mostly for balance. Most have humanlike hands with opposable thumbs— that is, the thumb can be placed opposite any of the fingers. Only the colobus is thumbless. (*See* COLOBUS.)

New World monkeys are native to Central and South America. They have 36 teeth and widely-spaced nostrils. Many have prehensile tails which can be used to grasp branches or other objects. Their thumbs are only partially opposable, offering less flexibility than the hands of the Old World monkeys. Two species, the spider monkey and the woolly spider monkey, are thumbless. (*See* SPIDER MONKEY.) All of the New World monkeys are arboreal, living in the trees. The New World monkeys belong to two families. Family Callitrichidae includes the marmosets and tamarins. These monkeys have 32 teeth after the four wisdom teeth usually waste away early in life. They are the only monkeys with claws instead of nails on their fingers and toes. All other New World monkeys belong to the family Cebidae. These include the capuchin, howler monkey, spider monkey, squirrel monkey, and woolly monkey.

Monkeys usually live in well-organized social groups. Family groups consist of one adult male, one adult female, and their young. Multimale groups consist of several adult males, about twice as many females, and their young. Single male groups consist of one adult male, several adult females, and their young. Often these groups establish a territory which then becomes off-limits to outsiders. (*See* DOMINANCE.) Monkeys frequently show affection by grooming each other.

Because of their similarities to human beings, monkeys are often used in medical and psychological research. Many of the natural living areas of monkeys have been destroyed by people. As a result, several species are endangered and may soon be extinct. *See also* HOWLER MONKEY; MAMMAL; PROBOSCIS MONKEY; PSYCHOLOGY.   A.J.C./J.J.M.

MONKEY PUZZLE (məng′ kē pəz′ əl) The monkey puzzle tree (*Araucaria araucana*) is an evergreen conifer. (*See* CONIFER.) It belongs to the family Araucaria which includes about 16 coniferous species, all of which grow south of the equator. The monkey puzzle tree may reach a height of 50 m [165 ft]. Sharp, needlelike leaves grow in dense whorls on stiff, crooked branches. (*See* LEAF.) These branches grow in whorls around the trunk. The monkey puzzle is so named because the sharp leaves and tangled branches make it difficult to climb.   A.J.C./M.H.S.

MONOCARPIC PLANT (män′ ə kär′ pik plant) A monocarpic plant is any plant that dies after once producing flowers and fruits. The term may apply to annual or biennial plants, but it is usually reserved for those plants that live for several years before flowering. The bamboo, for example, may live for 100 years before producing any flowers. (*See* BAMBOO.) *See also* AGAVE.   A.J.C./E.R.L.

MONOCOTYLEDON (män′ ə kät əl ēd′ ən) A monocotyledon is any of about 40,000 species of flowering plants that produce seeds containing only one cotyledon. (*See* COTYLEDON.) Their vascular tissue (xylem and phloem) is in scattered bundles in the stem.

The flowers usually have structures (such as petals, sepals, stamens, and pistils) in multiples of 3. The leaves are usually simple with parallel venation. (*See* LEAF.) There is no cambium or lateral meristem, so the stem never increases in thickness. There are no annual rings and there is no woody tissue. (*See* MERISTEM.) Most monocotyledons are herbaceous plants. They usually have fibrous roots. (*See* ROOT.)

Some familiar monocotyledons are corn, grasses, cereal crops, and members of the lily, palm, iris, and orchid families. *See also* ANGIOSPERM; DICOTYLEDON.   A.J.C./M.H.S.

The arrowhead is so called because of the shape of its leaves, which have the characteristic parallel veins of monocotyledons.

MONOECIOUS (mə nē′ shəs) A monoecious plant is one which has both male flowers (staminate) and female flowers (pistillate) on the same plant. (*See* FLOWER.) They are different from dioecious plants in which each plant has either staminate flowers or pistillate flowers, but not both. Most conifers are monoecious, as are members of the beech, birch, and hazel families. *See also* DIOECIOUS.   A.J.C./M.H.S.

MONONUCLEOSIS (män′ ō nü′ klē ō′ səs) Mononucleosis, or infectious mononucleosis, is a disease caused by a virus. The infection causes fever, sore throat, aching muscles, and swelling of the lymph glands, particularly those glands in the neck. The liver and the spleen may also enlarge. Sometimes there is a rash. When the blood is examined, there are large numbers of the blood cells called monocytes. A person with the disease may feel sick for many months. *See also* BLOOD; VIRUS.   D.M.H.W./J.J.F.

MONORAIL (män′ ə rāl′) A monorail is a railroad that has only one rail. Monorail cars run on a rail that is placed above or below them. Cars that run above the track have either a gyroscopic device to balance them or guide wheels that grip the sides of the rail and keep the cars from falling over. (*See* GYROSCOPE.)

There are two types of suspended monorail systems. In the older system, the cars hang from wheels on a rail. The newer "split rail" type suspends the cars from two rails spaced closely together and housed in one enclosure. The enclosure keeps the rails dry and reduces the noise of the trains.

Monorail cars can be powered by electric motors, gas turbines, or gasoline engines. Rubber wheels are generally used to reduce noise. Monorails are faster and cheaper to operate and maintain than two-rail elevated or subway lines. The smaller amount of fric-

The suspended monorail (left) takes up little space and can be built over an existing road. The Japanese supported monorail train (below) has guide wheels to keep it stable. Monorail trains are quiet and inexpensive.

tion in monorails allows greater speeds and lower operating costs.

The first monorail was built in 1901 in Wuppertal, Germany. It is still carrying passengers. Many cities in the United States have studied the possibilities of monorail systems. They are attractive to busy cities because they can be built quickly and they operate above crowded city streets. Also, ground supports require little space because they have only one rail to support.

The first monorail in the U.S. began operating in 1956 in Houston, Texas. Other monorails are located at the "Disneylands" in Anaheim, California, and Lake Buena Vista, in Florida. Monorails are also operating in Dallas, Texas; Seattle, Washington; Lake Arrowhead, California; and Pomona, California. In 1964 Japan built a 13.2 km [8.2 mi] monorail in Tokyo for the Olympic Games that were held there that year. Also, Montreal built a monorail in 1967 for a World's Fair.

The invention of air cushion vehicles that travel on a cushion of air has led to new ideas for monorails. Wheelless hovertrains have been designed in England and France. They run along the top of a girder and are propelled by jet engines or magnetic force. A monorail in Germany uses magnetic force to raise the train above a single rail.   W.R.P./R.W.L.

MONOTREME (män′ ə trēm′) Monotremes are a group of primitive mammals. Like reptiles, monotremes lay eggs. Yet

The platypus is one of the monotremes, the most primitive group of mammals. Like reptiles, from which they and other mammals evolved, monotremes lay eggs, but like more advanced mammals they have hair and the females suckle their young.

monotremes are true mammals—they have hair and the females nurse their young with milk. The platypus and the spiny anteater (echidna) are the only monotremes in existence. Monotremes are restricted in their range to Australia, Tasmania, and New Guinea.

Some mammalogists think that monotremes represent a distinct line of mammalian evolution, separate from the marsupials and placentals. The skeletal structures of some monotremes and their stance are more closely related to reptiles than to mammals. *See also* ECHIDNA; MAMMAL; REPTILE; PLATYPUS.

J.J.A./J.J.M.

MONSOON (män sün′) Monsoons are winds that blow onshore during the summer and offshore during the winter. The best-known monsoons occur in the northern region of the Indian Ocean.

Monsoons are caused by the unequal heating of land and sea. During the summer, the land is warmer than the sea. The warm conti-

nental air rises and is replaced by moist air from the ocean. This moist air produces the heavy rain associated with monsoons.

During the winter, the oceans are warmer than the land. The warm ocean air rises and is replaced by cooler, dry continental air.

Monsoon winds generally blow onshore from April to October. In the northern Indian Ocean area, they bring heavy rains to otherwise dry places. Monsoons occur on a smaller scale in Africa, Australia, China, Spain, and the United States. *See also* INSOLATION; CLIMATE.

J.M.C./C.R.

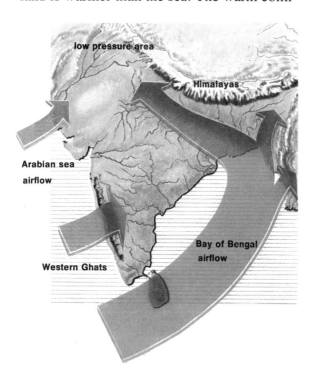

The monsoon winds blow over the Indian subcontinent from April to September. The monsoons bring rain to otherwise dry areas.

MOON

The moon (mün) is the only natural satellite of the earth. It is a barren, round body with no atmosphere, no water, and no life. The moon is the brightest object in the night sky. It is the only heavenly body to be visited by people.

Lunar statistics The moon has a diameter of about 3,476 km [2,160 mi]. The moon rotates on its own axis as it orbits the earth. It takes the moon slightly more than 27 days to make one complete turn on its axis. One trip around the earth takes the moon about 29½ days. The lunar day and night are each about 14 earth-days long. The moon's gravity is about one-sixth of the earth's gravity. This means that a person who weighs 80 kg [180 lb] on earth would weigh about 15 kg [30 lb] on the moon. The gravity of the moon is too weak to hold an atmosphere around it. Since it lacks an atmosphere, the moon has great changes in temperature. The temperature during the lunar day may go beyond 100°C [212°F]. At night, the temperature goes down to −173°C [−280°F].

Lunar movement The moon follows an elliptical (oval-shaped) orbit around the earth.

Above, a photograph of the moon taken by the U.S. spacecraft Apollo 8 shows the Sea of Crisis (left), and the crater Langrenus (bottom left corner).

Above, a photomicrograph of a thin section of moon rock illuminated by polarized light.

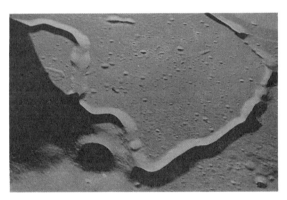

Above, the Hadley Rille and St. George Crater.

The St. George Crater from the surface of the moon.

Footprints in the Sea of Storms, made during the Apollo 12 mission.

Left, Neil Armstrong, the first man to set foot on the moon, took this photo of Edwin Aldrin, the second man, descending the ladder of the Apollo 11 lunar module on July 20, 1969.

The moon moves from west to east around the sun. From the earth, however, it seems to move from east to west. This is because the earth spins faster than the moon moves.

The moon's distance from the earth varies because of its elliptical orbit. The moon is closest to the earth at a point called the perigee. At the perigee, the moon is about 356,399 km [221,456 mi] away from the earth. At a point called the apogee, the moon is 406,699 km [252,711 mi] from the earth. The apogee is the greatest distance that occurs between the moon and the earth.

The moon creates no light of its own. Instead, it reflects the sun's light. This light is visible from the earth in varying amounts during periods called phases.

When the moon is between the sun and the earth, only the side of the moon facing the sun is lit. The unlit side faces the earth in a phase called the new moon. Light reflected from the earth to the moon may dimly light the moon.

This reflected light is called earthshine.

A little more of the moon becomes visible each day following the new moon phase. At first, a small slit of light appears at the moon's eastern edge. The apparent line between the dark side and the sunlit side of the moon is called the terminator. The terminator gradually moves west. After a week, half a lunar hemisphere is visible from earth. This phase is called the first quarter. After another week, the earth is located between the sun and the moon. At this point, an entire lunar hemisphere is visible from the earth. This phase is called the full moon. The moon is said to be "waxing" between the new moon phase and the full moon phase.

About seven days after the full moon, only half the full moon is visible. This phase is called the last quarter. About one week after the last quarter, the moon returns to the new moon phase.

The moon is said to be waning between

the full moon phase and the new moon phase. The time between new moon phases is called the synodic month.

The moon occasionally passes through positions in which it is darkened by the earth's shadow. At other times the moon blocks the sun's rays from reaching a small area on the earth's surface. Such events are called eclipses. (*See* ECLIPSE.)

The lunar surface   The moon is covered with vast plains, high mountains, and deep craters. From earth the lunar plains look like dark patches. The plains are called maria (Latin for "seas"). The maria were filled billions of years ago by great lava flows. (*See* LAVA.)

The lunar mountains appear grayish from the earth. The mountains are called highlands. Some of the highlands are over 7,920 m [26,000 ft] tall.

Craters are the most characteristic feature of the moon. Scientists think that there may be more than 500,000 craters greater than 1.6 km [1 m] wide. There are many billion craters at least 30 cm [1 ft] wide. The largest crater is about 1,100 km [700 mi] wide.

The smaller craters may have been caused by meteoroids colliding with the lunar surface. Since there is no atmosphere to produce friction, the meteoroids hit the moon full force. (*See* METEOR.)

The huge craters on the moon may have formed by collisions with asteroids. A few craters seem to indicate past volcanic activity.

Valleys on the moon are called rilles. Rilles may be faults in the moon's crust. The winding rilles were probably formed by lava flows.

Scientists have determined that the lunar soil is made of rock and glass chunks. The soil on the maria is from 1.5 to 6 m [5 to 20 ft] deep. The lunar soil does not support earth plants, but seems to help them grow better when combined with earth soil. No evidence of past or present life was detected in the lunar soil. (*See* EXOBIOLOGY.)

The moon rocks seem to have no new elements. They are made of minerals made up of aluminum, calcium, iron, magnesium, oxygen, silicon, and titanium.

There are two main types of moon rocks brought back by the astronauts: basalt and breccia. Basalt is hardened lava. The minerals that make up the basalt formed at temperatures of about 1,200°C [2,200°F]. Breccia is composed of soil and rock fragments cemented together.

Formation of the moon   There are several theories that attempt to explain how the moon was made. One theory says that the earth and the moon were once one planet. Eventually, the gravitational pull of the sun caused a huge bulge to stick out from the earth. The bulge separated from the earth and became the moon. Most astronomers do not consider this theory a likely explanation.

Another theory says that the moon was a separate planet that became trapped in orbit around the earth.

The third theory says that the earth and moon formed at the same time from gases and dust remaining from the sun's formation. This theory seems the most logical to astronomers. (*See* COSMOLOGY.)

Lunar exploration   In the late 1950s and early 1960s, Russian and American space probes transmitted photographs of the moon back to earth. On July 20, 1969, the Apollo 11 astronaut Neil Armstrong became the first person to set foot on the moon. Several other lunar explorations from the United States followed, during which many experiments were conducted. 400 kg [881 lb] of moon rocks were collected during these Apollo missions. The data obtained has vastly increased our knowledge of the moon. Astronauts recorded magnetic readings much higher than predicted. This may mean that the moon has a liquid core, somewhat like the earth's core.

The astronauts left seismometers on the

lunar surface to detect and measure "moon-quakes." The seismometers determined that the moon vibrates like a ringing bell when hit by a meteoroid. This information suggests that the moon's interior is different from the earth's. (*See* SEISMOLOGY.)

By international agreement, the moon may not be used for military reasons. This agreement allows the peaceful exploration and possible colonization of the earth's closest neighbor. *See also* NASA; SPACE TRAVEL; TIDE. J.M.C./C.R.

MOOSE (müs) The moose (*Alces alces*) is the largest member of the deer family. It stands about 2.3 m [7.5 ft] at the shoulder. Moose live in the northern regions of Europe and North America. Outside of America, these animals are known as elk, not moose. (*See* ELK.) But the American elk is different. The correct name for the American elk is wapiti. Moose like to live in forest land containing swamps and lakes.

The moose has high shoulders that look like a hump. The bell is another unusual feature of the moose. The bell is a growth of skin covered with hair. It hangs underneath the moose's throat. The animal is brownish black on the upper parts, with gray or grayish brown covering the belly and gray to white on the lower parts of the legs.

The bull (male) has heavy, flattened antlers. Each antler has short points, which stick out like fingers from the palm of a hand. The antlers are shed every year, and a new pair is grown. The antlers are full-grown by late August and may weigh more than 45 kg [100 lb]. The bull moose then strips off the dead skin ("velvet") on the antlers. The animal polishes his antlers against trees. The antlers are used as weapons.

The mating season of the moose lasts from four to eight weeks in the fall. Baby moose are born about seven months later, usually in late May or June. A cow (female moose) may have one calf, twins, or (very rarely) triplets.

Moose remain alone in summer. During winter, they tend to stay together in small bands in swamps. The swamps and woods give protection from the cold winds. With their long legs, moose can walk easily in deep snow as they nibble on the twigs of trees.

At one time, hunters nearly killed all the moose in the northeastern United States. In both the United States and Canada, moose are protected by law. J.J.A./J.J.M.

This bull moose has its palmate antlers "in velvet." The moose is the largest member of the deer family, standing nearly 2.3 m [7.5 ft] at the shoulder when full grown. The antlers by themselves may weigh more than 45 kg [100 lb].

MORAINE (mə rān') A moraine is an accumulation of rock and soil that is deposited by a receding (melting) glacier or ice sheet.

There are several kinds of morains. A lateral moraine is formed by rocks that fall onto a glacier as it passes through a mountain valley. When two valley glaciers combine, a medial moraine forms by the merging of two lateral moraines.

A terminal moraine is a ridge that is deposited at the edge of a melting glacier or ice sheet. Smaller terminal moraines are deposited when a glacier stops temporarily during its retreat. Terminal moraines often form ranges of low hills.

Material that is deposited beneath a glacier as it melts is called a ground moraine. *See also* GLACIATION; GLACIER AND ICE SHEET. J.M.C./W.R.S.

Rocks broken up by the movement of ice have formed a lateral moraine (left of picture).

MORGAN, THOMAS HUNT (1866–1945)

Thomas Morgan (mȯr′ gən) was an American biologist who made discoveries in genetics. (*See* GENETICS.) Scientists knew that certain characteristics of an animal are passed down from parents to their young. This is called heredity. For example, the color of hair or eyes of a parent can be passed down to its child. Scientists had suggested that heredity was controlled by tiny particles. But nothing was known about them. Morgan discovered these tiny particles. They are now called genes. He experimented with a small fly called *Drosophila*. This insect has large chromosomes in its salivary glands. Morgan showed that these chromosomes contained the fly's genes. He was even able to show the position of the genes in the chromosomes. For this work, Morgan won the 1933 Nobel Prize in Medicine and Physiology.   M.E./D.G.F.

MORNING GLORY (mȯr′ ning glōr′ ē)

Morning glory is the name of a family of about 300 climbing plants that live in moderate to warm climates throughout the world. The garden morning glory is one of the best-known plants in this group. Others are the bindweed, jalap, moonflower, scammony, and sweet potato.

The morning glory gets it name from the fact that its fragrant, funnel-shaped flowers open in the morning. They close later in the day when sunlight becomes stronger. The morning glory plant grows rapidly and twines about nearby objects. It grows from 3 to 6 m [10 to 20 ft] high, and is widely used as a covering for fences, posts, and porches. The garden morning glory has dark green heart-shaped leaves. The flowers are various shades of blue, purple, red, pink, and white.

Japanese varieties have flowers that are 18 cm [7 in] in diameter. The root of a Mexican species, called jalap, supplies the laxative known as jalap.   W.R.P./M.H.S.

MORPHOLOGY (mȯr fäl′ ə jē)

Morphology is the branch of biology that deals with the size, shape, and structure of living things. It studies the external development of an organism, the relationships of its internal structures, and the similarities and differences between several types of the same organism. *See also* BIOLOGY.   A.J.C./E.R.L.

MORSE, SAMUEL FINLEY BREESE (1791–1872)

Samuel Morse (mȯrs) was the inventor of the telegraph. He also invented a code for sending messages along a telegraph cable. It is called the Morse code. (*See* MORSE CODE.)

Morse was not trained as an engineer. He was trained as an artist. He was born in Charlestown, Massachusetts, and studied painting in England. He returned to the United States in 1832. Earlier he had seen the demonstration of an effect in physics called electromagnetism. (*See* ELECTROMAGNETISM.) The demonstration interested him and he started to study electromagnetism. In 1837 he demonstrated his first telegraph in New York. However there was little interest in it. Finally, in 1840 the American government granted him a patent for his invention. Two years later he laid a cable at the bottom of New York harbor for another demonstration. The demonstration failed because the cable was cut by a ship's anchor. In 1844 he built a telegraph between Washington and Baltimore. On May 24, 1844 the first telegraph message in the world was sent from Washington. The message was "What hath God wrought!" *See also* TELEGRAPH.

M.E./D.G.F.

MORSE CODE (mȯrs kōd) Morse code is a system of sounds that telegraphers and radio operators use to send messages by wire and radio. The code is a system of dots (short signals), dashes (long signals), and spaces. Each letter of the alphabet, plus numbers and other symbols, are represented by groups of dots and dashes. The Morse code is named for Samuel Morse, who patented the telegraph in 1840.

Telegraph messages are sent by pressing down on a telegraph key. The dot is made by pressing down the key and releasing it quickly. This produces a rapid "click-clack" sound in the receiver at the other end of the wire, or the radio receiver. In the case of radio telegraph, the sound is more like a musical note. A short dash is held twice as long as a

In 1837, Samuel Morse demonstrated the first telegraph. The code system of dots and dashes, which were sent by the primitive looking equipment pictured here, is still in use today. Below right is a sample of the international Morse code.

dot. A long dash is equal to four dots. The space between letters equals three dots. A space that is part of a letter combination equals two dots. Ships at sea sometimes send and receive radio telegraph messages.

For many years all telegraph messages and most news were transmitted by Morse code. Today most of these messages are sent by automatic printing telegraph machines called teleprinters and by automatic facsimile.

Morse code is used in the United States and Canada. Telegraph and radio operators in other countries use the International Morse Code. *See also* TELEGRAPH; TELEPRINTER.

W.R.P./R.W.L.

MORTAR (mȯrt′ ər) Mortar is the material used in bricklaying for joining bricks together. The mortar holds the bricks in position and creates a tight wall. The mortar is applied in a paste-like form. It gradually dries—partly by chemical reaction and partly by evaporation—to form a firm bond between the bricks.

Mortar usually contains portland cement for strength, hydrated lime for workability of the mixture, and sand for economy and volume. Water is added to create the chemical

THE INTERNATIONAL MORSE CODE

a b c d e f
g h i j k
l m n o p
q r s t u
v w x y
z

Numerals

1 2 3
4 5 6 7
8 9 0

reaction and to make the mixture easy to handle. A common mixture of mortar consists of one part cement, one part lime, six parts sand, and enough water to make a pastelike consistency. The lime in the mixture reduces the chances of cracking after the mortar has dried.   W.R.P./A.D.

MOSQUITO (mə skēt′ ō) A mosquito is any of about 2,500 species of flies belonging to 100 genera of the family Culicidae. (*See* FLY.) Most mosquitoes have slender bodies that are 3 to 6 mm [0.1 to 0.2 in] long and covered with tiny hairs and scales. The mosquito body is divided into three sections: head, thorax, and abdomen. The head has two huge, compound eyes, a long, tubelike proboscis, and two threadlike antennae. The antennae of the male are bushier than those of the female. The thorax has six jointed legs, each of which has a pair of claws. There are two wings which are very thin and almost transparent, with scaly wing veins. The thorax also has two pairs of spiracles for breathing. (*See* SPIRACLE.) The abdomen has eight pairs of spiracles. The female's abdomen ends in a tubelike ovipositor used for laying eggs.

Only the female mosquito is a bloodsucker. Different species of mosquitoes are host-specific, usually attacking only one kind of mammal, reptile, fish, bird, or amphibian. The beaklike proboscis of the female has six needlelike stylets which are used to pierce the skin of the victim. The female then squirts saliva into the wound to keep the blood from clotting. Most people are allergic to this saliva and it produces an itchy, red swelling. Some females suck more than their own weight in blood from a victim. The blood is needed so that the eggs within the female's body can mature and begin to develop. Mosquitoes are often attracted to a victim by body odor and warmth. A male mosquito does not attack animals, but sucks water and plant juices through its proboscis, as does the female at times.

Female mosquitoes attract mates by a high-pitched humming sound created by the beating of their wings. Different species beat their wings at different speeds, and males of their own species respond to that sound. The wing may beat as much as 1,000 times per second. After mating, the female lays as many as 300 eggs either singly or in clusters called rafts. The eggs are laid in or near some type of water. Each species has its preferred habitat. A single female may lay more than 3,000 eggs during her one-month lifetime. In warm weather, the eggs hatch into larvae in two or three days. These larvae are aquatic and are so active that they are often called wrigglers. These wrigglers live underwater and breathe through a special tubelike siphon or a pair of plates at the rear of the body. The wriggler feeds on tiny plants and animals and may even feed on mosquitoes or other wrigglers. The wriggler molts four times in the next few days before becoming a pupa. (*See* MOLTING.) The pupa is also aquatic and is called a tumbler because it tumbles around in the water. The pupa does not eat. Within four days, it develops into an adult. (*See* METAMORPHOSIS.)

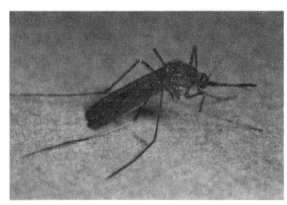

Above, a female malaria mosquito in its characteristic resting position.

There are three main genera of mosquitoes that attack human beings. Members of the genus *Culex* have clear, unspotted wings. They rest with their bodies parallel to the surface and their heads bent down at an angle to the body. *Culex* are the commonest mosquitoes in the United States and sometimes carry the disease encephalitis. Members of the genus *Anopheles* have spotted wings. They hold their heads and bodies in a straight line at an angle to the surface. *Anopheles* are the only mosquitoes that carry malaria. (*See* MALARIA.) Members of the genus *Aedes* rest in a position similar to that of *Culex*. Their wings are usually lightly tinted, however, and their thoraxes are silvery in color. *Aedes* may carry encephalitis or yellow fever. (*See* YELLOW FEVER.) Mosquitoes can be controlled by using insecticides or by eliminating breeding sites. *See also* INSECT.

A.J.C./J.E.R.

MOSS AND LIVERWORT Mosses (mòs′ iz) and liverworts (liv′ ər wərts′) are small green plants that belong to the phylum Bryophyta of the plant kingdom. Most bryophytes have tiny stems and leaves, though some liverworts are seaweedlike creeping plants. Although the bryophytes do not have true roots, they do have rootlike hairs called rhizoids. The rhizoids anchor the plant to the ground, and absorb water and minerals from the soil.

Most mosses and liverworts grow in damp places. Some mosses, though, are found even in hot, dry climates. Because the bryophytes are such simple plants, it is thought that they may have been among the first land plants to have evolved. (*See* EVOLUTION.)

Most bryophytes have a sexually repro-

Marchantia is a simple liverwort that can reproduce either sexually or asexually. Male and female organs develop on separate plants. "Gemma cups" are small buds that grow on the plant.

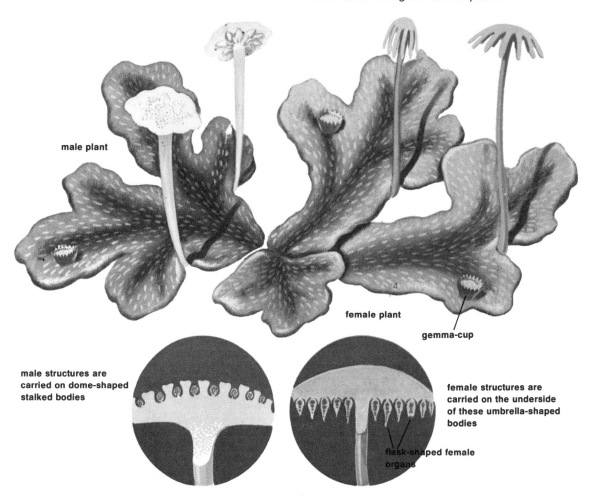

male plant

female plant

gemma-cup

male structures are carried on dome-shaped stalked bodies

female structures are carried on the underside of these umbrella-shaped bodies

flask-shaped female organs

ductive stage which alternates with an asexually reproductive stage. (*See* ALTERNATION OF GENERATIONS.) The gametophyte, or sexually reproductive stage, produces antheridia and archegonia. The antheridium is the male structure and produces flagellated antherozoids, or sperm. (*See* ANTHERIDIUM.) The archegonium is the female structure and produces ova, or eggs. (*See* ARCHEGONIUM.) When released, the antherozoids swim through the surface moisture to the archegonium. Once inside the archegonium, they fertilize the ova. Each fertilized egg then grows into an asexually reproductive sporophyte. The sporophyte produces a sporangium, or sporefilled capsule.

The moss sporangium contains chlorophyll. When the spores are mature, a protective cap falls from the capsule, revealing a ring of water-sensitive flaps. In dry weather, the flaps curl backward and allow the spores to scatter in the wind. In damp weather, the flaps stay closed, preventing the spores from getting wet. The liverwort capsule is much simpler and does not contain chlorophyll. When the spores mature, the capsule splits open, releasing the spores. When the spores land on a moist surface, they swell and begin to grow. Moss spores produce a slender green thread called a protonema. The protonema branches and produces several new moss plants. As a result, moss usually forms clusters or cushions which increase in size as new protonema grow from the bases of the old ones. Liverwort spores do not produce protonema, but grow directly into new liverwort plants.

Mosses and liverworts are important plants for several reasons. The rhizoids break off tiny bits of rock which, when added to dead plant tissue, become soil. (*See* SOIL.) In addition, the rhizoids help keep the soil from eroding. (*See* SOIL EROSION.) These plants also help keep water in the soil, keeping it damp and preventing floods. Peat moss, or sphagnum, is moss that grows in layers over other layers of dead moss. (*See* PEAT.) In the United States, frontiersmen used to fill cracks in their log cabins with moss. In some countries, parents line their infants' cradles with moss. This provides warmth, softness, and protection for the baby. In some countries, moss is mixed with reindeer hair and used to stuff mattresses. A.J.C./M.H.S.

The hair moss grows in damp places on moors and heaths. The sporangium is initially covered by a small pointed cap. However, this is shed when the spores are released.

MOSS ANIMAL (mȯs′ an′ ə məl) A moss animal is any of about 3,500 species of tiny, aquatic, invertebrate animals belonging to the phylum Bryozoa. This phylum is sometimes called Ectoprocta or Polyzoa. Most moss animals live in colonies on underwater objects in the oceans. There are, however, several freshwater species. Moss animals are so named because some of their colonies look like moss.

An individual moss animal is called a zooid. Each zooid is about 1 mm [0.04 in] long, though colonies may reach a length of 1 m [40 in] or more. Each zooid lives in a hard, chitinous case called a zooecium. (*See* CHITIN.) The zooid gathers food by means of ciliated tentacles which circle the mouth. If disturbed, the zooid can retreat into the zooecium for protection.

Moss animals are hermaphrodites. (*See* HERMAPHRODITE.) They reproduce both sexually and asexually. The larva settles on a surface and metamorphosizes into a zooid. (*See* METAMORPHOSIS.) The zooid then produces several asexual buds, each of which develops into another zooid. (*See* BUDDING.) The adult zooids are sessile, usually staying attached to one surface for their entire lives.

Moss animals have relatively short lives. Death may be caused by the break-up of the zooid when it releases larvae. The shell-like containers left by the moss animals (and their ancestors—15,000 extinct species) are the source of many of the limestone deposits in the seas. *See also* INVERTEBRATE.

A.J.C./C.S.H.

MOTION PICTURE

Motion pictures (mō′ shən pik′ chər) are a series of pictures projected onto a screen in quick succession to give the eye an impression of continuous movement. This impression occurs because of a phenomenon known as persistence of vision, in which the eye keeps the image—for a moment—of what it has seen. As a result, if the projected moving pictures follow each other fast enough, the eye will join them together to form a continuous image. Each separate picture, or frame, is slightly different from the previous one. Early cameras and projectors operated at 16 frames per second. This caused a flickering effect, and objects seemed to be moving faster than normal. Today, films operate at 24 frames per second, which eliminates the flickering problems.

Motion picture cameras usually take pictures at the same speed as they are going to be projected. For slow motion pictures, many more frames are shot each second. To speed up events on the film, like showing the opening of a flower, for example, one frame is shot every few seconds, or even minutes.

Film for motion picture cameras is a flexible strip of celluloid coated with chemicals that are sensitive to light. Both black-and-white and color film can be used in the standard moving picture camera. Motion picture film is made in several widths, which are expressed in millimeters. Film widths for movies shown in theaters are either 35 mm [about 1.37 in], or 70 mm [about 2.75 in]. Most film for use in schools is 16 mm [0.63 in]. Most home movies are 8 mm [about 0.25 in].

The sound track of a motion picture is contained in a narrow band along one edge of the film. Sometimes, in the case of special large-screen movies shown in theaters, the sound track is on a separate piece of film. The narrow band varies in width and density. A light shining through the band produces a varying signal in a photoelectric cell. The electrical output of the cell is then amplified to produce the sound track of the movie. The sound track can also be contained in a magnetic strip that runs along the edge of the film. A magnetic sound track is of higher quality than the film type.

Several systems have been developed to increase the size and realism of motion pictures. Cinerama, introduced in 1952, was shown on a wide, curved screen. The film was shot from three separate camera angles, and it used seven-channel stereo sound. In the CinemaScope and Todd-AO systems, the camera ''squeezed'' a wide image onto 35mm film. The projector, in turn, reversed the process and projected the image onto a wide screen. CinemaScope and Todd-AO both had stereo sound.

These systems involved extra production expense, and often required modification in equipment at the theaters. Although the systems drifted out of general use, some of the technical advances they first utilized were incorporated into conventional filming and projection equipment.

Thomas Alva Edison, an American inventor, is generally credited with inventing motion pictures in 1889. Previously Hannibal W. Goodwin, an American clergyman, had introduced a transparent celluloid film. Goodwin's film was tough and flexible, and able to

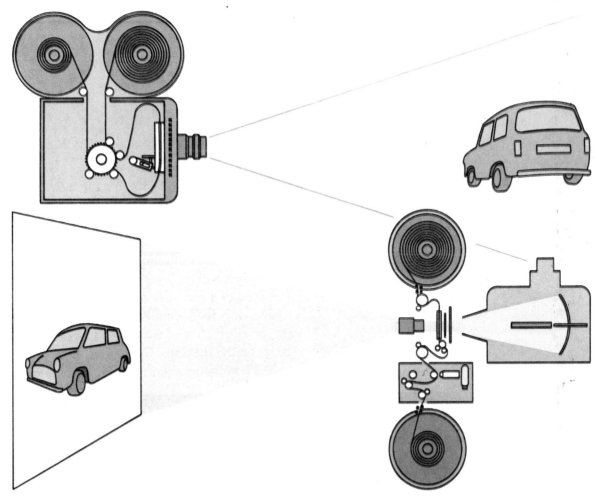

Motion pictures are made by taking a series of photographs of the subject in rapid succession. In the camera the film is passed in front of the aperture by a series of rollers. The shutter opens and closes at regular intervals—24 times per second—and the film is stopped briefly each time a picture is taken. When the film has been developed it can be run through a projector. A strong light is focused by a concave mirror onto the film and the image is projected onto a screen using a lens. A rapid sequence of pictures is cast onto the screen, giving the viewer an impression of movement.

withstand the rigors of being wound on spools and run through cameras. Until that time, there had been no way to take pictures that could run quickly through a camera. Edison called his device a kinetoscope. It was a wooden cabinet in which 15 m [50 ft] of film revolved on spools. A person looked through a peephole to watch the pictures move.

Motion pictures were projected onto a screen for the first time in 1895, in Paris, France. A year later, in 1896, Edison introduced a projecting version of his kinetoscope. He held a public exhibition in New York City, and showed scenes of a prize fight, a performance by a dancer, and waves rolling onto a beach. By 1900, movies had become a popular entertainment in music halls and vaudeville theaters across the country. There was no sound. Dialogue was shown on the screen as printed matter, usually white type on black background, interrupting the flow of action just long enough for a few words to be read to help understand the plot. Sometimes a piano player or organist in the theater played live background music.

Hollywood, California, soon became the movie capital of the world. Several major studios were established there in the early

1920s, including Metro-Goldwyn-Mayer (MGM), Warner Brothers, Universal, and Fox. In 1927, Warner Brothers changed the industry almost overnight when it released the first talking picture. It was ''The Jazz Singer,'' and it starred the famous vaudeville star, Al Jolson. Jolson sang a few songs and spoke a few lines of dialogue in the film. Soon after that, only talking pictures were made. The industry began to flourish, and it rapidly grew into an important part of the American way of life.

Animated films, often called cartoons, are made by using artwork instead of photography. Movements are created in sequences of individual drawings. Each individual piece varies slightly from the preceding one in the direction of the movement being depicted. The drawings are done on a transparent material called a cel. The film is made frame by frame by photographing each cel against a stationary background. Some of today's animation is now done by specially programmed computers.

The usefulness of motion pictures goes beyond entertainment. Schools, industries, and governments use film to instruct and inform. For example, many young people learn about the basics of automobile driving without using a real car. A system of auto controls is linked to a film—or a computer-generated image—of road conditions. The would-be driver is given a sense of what it is like to be actually driving. Systems like this are called simulators, and they are used to train

With the coming of the Space Age, there were a large number of motion pictures that had spectacular special effects. The photograph below shows the filming of one such effect from the film *Return of the Jedi.*

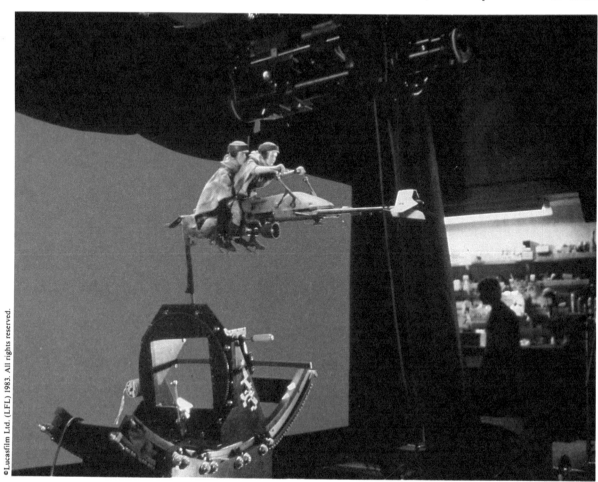

Early cinematograph projectors had to be operated by hand, because there was no other way of controlling the speed of the film.

Shown above is a motion-picture editing table.

pilots, astronauts, police officers, fire fighters, and others in professions in which training mistakes could be costly or dangerous. (*See* SIMULATOR.)

The beginning of television as a mass medium in the 1940s and 1950s seemed to be a major threat to the motion picture industry. Many thought that if free entertainment was available, people would not pay for admission to motion picture theaters. While admissions did drop for a time in the 1950s, their dollar value nearly tripled between 1960 and 1980. In the same time, the dollar value of radio and television receivers and phonograph records increased almost seven times.

W.R.P./R.W.L.

MOTORCYCLE (mō′ tər sī′ kəl) A motorcycle is a form of two-wheeled transport. A motorcycle works in a way very similar to an automobile. It has an internal-combustion engine. (*See* ENGINE.) In an internal-combustion engine, fuel is mixed with air in a cylinder. The fuel is ignited by a spark and it burns. As it burns, it produces a large amount of hot gases. These gases push a piston along the cylinder. The pushing of the piston provides the power for the wheels. Most motorcycles have either one or two cylinders. Racing motorcycles, like automobiles, sometimes have more than two cylinders. In an internal-combustion engine, the cylinders have to be kept cool. In most automobiles, water is used for this. In all but the largest motorcycles, air is used. The cylinders of motorcycles often have fins on the outside. This helps to keep them cooler.

Like automobiles, motorcycles have a device called a clutch. (*See* CLUTCH.) The clutch is operated by a hand lever. It disconnects the engine from the gear box. It is used when the rider is starting, stopping, or changing gear. Most motorcycles have three or four gears. Gear-changing is done by the feet. The clutch lever is on one side of the handle bars. On the

This modern motorcycle has many refinements, such as indicators and an automatic starter.

other side is a lever for the front brake. The back brake is operated by a foot pedal.

M.E./R.W.L.

MOUNTAIN (maŭnt′ ən) A mountain is an elevated region of land characterized by steep slopes, lofty peaks, and rugged terrain. Geologists generally agree that an altitude of at least 610 m [2,000 ft] above sea level, or a projection of 300 m [1,000 ft] above the surrounding land, is necessary for an area to be called mountainous.

Some important mountain ranges of the earth include the Rocky and Appalachian mountain ranges of North America, the Andes of South America, the Alps of Europe, and the Himalayas of Asia. The highest mountain peak on earth is Mount Everest. This Himalayan peak is 8,848 m [29,028 ft] above sea level.

Formation of mountains Most mountains form by faulting, folding, or volcanic activity. Mountains formed by vertical faults are called block mountains. Great blocks of rock are uplifted above the surrounding terrain because of vertical movements along faults. The mountains rise as great tilted blocks. The Sierra Nevada Mountains in California were formed by faulting. (*See* FAULT.)

Some of the earth's greatest mountain ranges were formed by folding. Folding is thought to occur in two different ways. One possible way is by geosynclinal folding. A geosyncline is a deep depression in the earth's crust, subject to downward movement. A great accumulation of sedimentary rock filled the geosynclines. Eventually, the sides of the geosynclines squeezed the rocks above the crust, thus forming mountains. As erosion wore away the tops of the mountains, more uplifting occurred to maintain isostatic balance. (*See* ISOSTACY.)

High mountain ranges, such as the Alps and the Himalayas, may have formed by folding due to the sideways movements of plates. (*See* PLATE TECTONICS.) According to the continental drift theory, the plates that compose the earth's crust are constantly moving. When two plates collide, marine sediment is forced up between them. The Himalayas formed when the plate that carries India collided with the Asian mainland plate. The collision forced the Indian plate under the Asian plate, forcing up the sediment between them. This theory also explains the discovery of marine fossils on the upper slopes of Mount Everest. (*See* CONTINENTAL DRIFT.) The Ap-

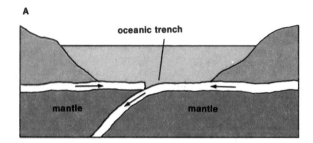

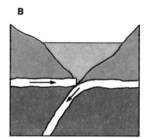

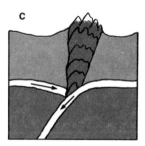

According to the theory of continental drift, fold mountains are formed by the collision of plates underlying the earth's crust (A). The land masses get closer (B) until they finally meet, squeezing sediments into a mountain range (C).

The Valais Alps in Switzerland are fold mountains. Geologists believe that they were raised up when a "plate" in the earth's crust bearing Italy was forced against Europe.

palachians may have formed in a similar way during an earlier time period.

Volcanic mountains are composed of hardened lava, ash, and other debris. This material is vomited from the earth during volcanic eruptions. Most volcanic mountains are basically cone-shaped with a hole or crater at the top.

Volcanic mountains may form in a very short period of time. Paricutin is a dormant (inactive) volcanic mountain that stands 2,500 m [8,200 ft] tall. It did not even exist before its eruption in a Mexican cornfield in 1943. The Hawaiian Islands are a chain of volcanic mountains. *See also* EROSION; VOLCANO.   J.M.C./W.R.S.

MOUNTAIN ASH (maûnt′ ən ash) A mountain ash is a flowering shrub that belongs to the genus *Sorbus*. It has roselike flowers and small orange berries. It is not related to the ash trees, which are common in North America. There is another tree called a mountain ash, but it is a eucalyptus from Australia. *See also* ASH; EUCALYPTUS.   S.R.G./M.H.S.

MOUSE (maûs) Mouse is a name given to many small kinds of rodents. There are hun-

dreds of types of mice. But the word "mouse" is not the name of any one kind of animal or family of animals. In general, a mouse is a small rodent with a body seldom exceeding 100 mm [4 in] in length. All mice (like all rodents) have chisellike front teeth. These teeth are useful for gnawing. A rodent's front teeth grow throughout its life. Mice are found in all parts of the world. Mice live in mountains, fields, woodlands, swamps, near streams, and in deserts.

The house mouse (*Mus musculus*) is probably the most widely known type of mouse. It lives wherever people live. The house mouse often builds its nest in houses, garages, or barns. All house mice climb well—they can be heard running between the walls of houses. House mice that live in fields and forests usually come out only at night. The body of a house mouse is about 6.4 to 8.9 cm [2.5 to 3.5 in] in length, not including the tail. The fur of most house mice is grayish brown on the back and sides, with a yellowish white fur covering the under parts. House mice raised as pets or for use in laboratories may have pure white fur, be spotted, or have a combination of colors. House mice feed on any grain, vegetable, or meat they can find, along with items such as leather, paste, soap, glue, and paper. A female house mouse may give birth every 20 or 30 days. She may give birth to from four to seven young at a time. Young mice stay near the nest for about three weeks after birth. Then they leave to build nests and start reproducing. Human beings are probably the main enemy of the house mouse.

The American harvest mouse (*Reithrodontomys fulvescens*) looks like a house mouse, but is smaller and has more hair on its tail. Harvest mice build their nests in places where tall grass grows. The grasshopper mouse (*Onychomys leucogaster*) is about the same size as the house mouse. But grasshopper mice look fatter and have stubby tails. These mice are so named because they eat grasshoppers. Grasshopper mice also eat insects, worms, scorpions, as well as other grasshopper mice. The deer mouse (*Peromyscus maniculatus*) is sometimes called a white-footed mouse. When excited, deer mice rapidly thump their feet on the ground, producing a noise like the rapid beats of a drum.   J.J.A./J.J.M.

MOVEMENT OF PLANTS (müv′ mənt uv plants) One of the differences between plants and animals is that most animals are able to move from one place to another under their own power while most plants stay in one place for their entire lives. Some plants, however, are able to move under their own power. Slime molds, for example, have as ameboid (amebalike) movement whereby they ''ooze'' from one place to another. (*See* SLIME MOLD.) Some types of algae have whiplike flagella which they use to paddle themselves through the water. (*See* ALGA.) Many plants, particularly the lower plants, produce mobile male gametes which swim about in order to find eggs to fertilize. Aside from these exceptions, plant movement is usually confined to the movement of certain structures while the plant itself stays fixed in one place.

There are three basic types of plant movement: tropisms, nutations, and nastic movements. A tropism is a growth response that is caused by a specific environmental stimulus. The direction of the growth is determined by the stimulus. A positive tropism is toward the stimulus. A negative tropism is away from the stimulus. Tropisms are caused by special growth hormones called auxins. (*See* HORMONE.) In most cases, the stimulus causes the auxins to collect on one side of an affected organ. This causes the cells on that side to grow and divide more quickly than the cells on the other side. As a result, the organ bends away from the side with the most auxins.

Tropisms are named according to their stimuli. Phototropism is a growth response to the stimulus of light. In phototropism, auxins are concentrated on the side away from the light. This causes structures such as stems and leaves to grow toward the light. (*See* LEAF.) This concentration of auxins on the dark side may be due to the fact that light inhibits or kills auxins on the lighted side. Roots are negatively phototropic and grow away from the light. Root cells seem to have an opposite reaction to the presence of auxins. A concentration of auxins causes slowed growth instead of the increased growth rate found in most of the above-ground structures.

Geotropism is a growth response to the stimulus of gravity of the earth. Roots show positive geotropism while stems show negative geotropism. Hydrotropism is a growth response to the stimulus of water. Roots show positive hydrotropism and often grow great distances toward areas of moist soil. Chemotropism is a growth response to a chemical stimulus. Traumatropism is a growth response to the stimulus of an injury or wound. It often results in a bending or curving of the affected organ. Thigmotropism is a growth response to touch or to a solid object. It can best be seen in vines and plants that produce tendrils. (*See* CLIMBING PLANT; TENDRIL.)

A nutation is a spiral growth pattern characteristic of the growing tips (roots, stems, flower stalks, etc.) of plants. It is a variation of tropic movements and is also caused by the changing distribution of auxins.

A nastic movement is sometimes called a turgor movement because it is caused by a change in the turgor pressure. Turgor pressure is the pressure of water in the cell. The direction of a nastic movement is not determined by the stimulus—that is, it is usually neither toward nor away from the stimulus. Nastic movements are also named according to their stimuli.

Photonasty is a turgor response to light. Thermonasty is a turgor response to temperature. These two nastic movements often interact in causing a response in a plant. The opening and closing of the stomates is an example of these two nastic movements. (*See* STOMA.) A plant's ''going to sleep'' at night is another example and is sometimes called nyctinasty.

Thigmonasty is a turgor response to touch or contact with a solid object. The Venus's flytrap (*Dionaea muscipula*), for example, shows thigmonasty when it captures an insect. (*See* CARNIVOROUS PLANT.) When an insect touches the sensitive hairs on the leaves forming the ''trap,'' the leaves snap shut, trapping the insect. This response takes less than a second and is caused by a rapid change in turgor pressure. When a leaf of the *Mimosa pudica* plant is touched, all the leaves go limp and droop. This turgor response also takes less than a second, but the plant may need 20 minutes to recover and return to normal. (*See* MIMOSA.)   A.J.C./M.H.S

Right, these seedlings were grown in light coming from one direction only. The shoots respond by growing toward the light (positive phototropism.)

MUCOUS MEMBRANE (myü′ kəs məm′ brān′) A mucous membrane is a thin, delicate layer of cells. Many of the chambers and cavities inside the body are covered with mucous membrane. There are special cells in the membrane that make and pour out a thin sticky fluid called mucus. The cells making mucus are called goblet cells. Mucus has many important uses in the body. Dust and bacteria get stuck in the mucus that covers the inside of the nose and windpipe. This stops harmful dust and bacteria from reaching the delicate lungs. Mucus helps the small lumps of food to pass through our intestines. (*See* ALIMENTARY CANAL.) The lumps of food get covered with mucus. They can then slide smoothly along the intestine. The insides of the tubes that carry urine from the kidneys to the bladder are covered with mucous membrane. The membrane stops the urine from destroying the tubes.   J.A./J.J.F.

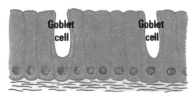

The mucous membrane is a delicate layer of cells that covers many of the surfaces of the body. The cross section shown illustrates the structure of the cells, including the goblet cells that make the mucus.

MUD PUPPY (məd′ pəp′ ē) A mud puppy is a large salamander that belongs to the family Necturidae. It lives in east-central North America. Mudpuppies grow to lengths from 20 to 33 cm [8 to 13 in]. Their bodies resemble that of a tadpole with legs. Mud puppies have large gills that stick out of their bodies near their necks. These gills are used by the salamander to breathe. (*See* GILLS.) The gills of the mud puppy are like those of the larvae of other salamanders and amphibians.

Mud puppies live in streams. They eat fish, crayfish, insects, and mollusks. (*See* MOLLUSCA.) In some parts of the United States, they are called water dogs. *See also* AMPHIBIAN; SALAMANDER.   S.R.G./R.L.L.

MULBERRY (məl' ber' ē) A mulberry is a medium-sized tree that may grow as tall as 21 m [70 ft]. There are four species found in North America. The paper mulberry and the red mulberry are native to the continent while the white mulberry and black mulberry have been imported from Asia. The leaves of the mulberry trees have unusual and varying shapes. One tree may have leaves with four lobes, leaves with two lobes, and leaves with no lobes at all. Mulberry trees produce fruit known as mulberries. Although only the red mulberry is usually eaten by people, all of the berries are eaten by wildlife.   S.R.G./M.H.S.

MULE (myül) The mule is a hybrid animal. It results from the mating of a mare (female horse) and a jackass (male donkey). (*See* ASS.) A mule combines the features of the two parents. Similar to the jackass, a mule has long ears, short mane, and a tail with a tuft of long hairs at the end. The father gives the mule surefootedness and endurance. Also like the jackass, a mule saves its strength. From the

Mules are hybrid animals. They are used mostly as pack animals in mountainous regions, because they are extremely sure-footed and can survive on relatively poor pasture.

mother, the mule gets a large, well-shaped body and strong muscles. The mare also gives the mule a horse's ease in getting used to harness.

The offspring of a male horse (stallion) and a female ass (jenny) is called a hinny. Mules do not have offspring of their own, except in extremely rare cases. All male mules and most females are sterile—that is, they cannot have offspring.

Mules resist diseases well. They remain strong even under harsh conditions. Because mules can bear rough treatment, they are useful for work in construction camps, mines, and military zones. In the United States, more than 90 percent of all the mules work on farms and plantations. Most mules are used in the southern states.   J.J.A./J.J.M.

MULLET (məl' ət) A mullet is a saltwater fish that belongs to the family Mugilidae. There are six species of mullet in North America. Although they are saltwater fish, two species are also found in fresh water— usually at the mouths of coastal rivers. All but one species live in the Atlantic Ocean. The other species is found in the Pacific Ocean.

Mullets are heavy-bodied, silvery fish. They are about 30 to 90 cm [1 to 3 ft] long. They eat small animals and plants.

S.R.G./E.C.M.

MULTIPLE SCLEROSIS (məl' tə pəl sklə rō' səs) Multiple sclerosis is a disease of the nervous system. Genes that control the body's immune system are associated with the disease. It is not known exactly what causes multiple sclerosis. No two people seem to be affected by it the same way.

The disease affects the central part of the nervous system (the brain and spinal cord). Nerves that are affected lose their covering of myelin. This is a fatty material that helps them to carry messages. (*See* NERVE CELL.) The nerves can no longer carry nerve impulses properly. The patient becomes weak and cannot move the muscles in some parts of his or her body. Different parts of the central nervous system are affected at different times. Sometimes parts that were affected seem to recover again. But gradually the disease gets worse and the patient becomes disabled. The disease may be fatal in some cases. In other cases, patients live into old age and eventually die from something quite different.

Multiple sclerosis commonly starts between the ages of 30 and 45, but it may start at any age. Even people who have been healthy all their lives may be affected. In about a third of patients, the first thing that is noticed is a temporary loss of sight in one eye. A complete recovery may occur and the loss of sight may not happen again for months or years. Later, other parts of the central nervous system are damaged. The person finds difficulty in walking, moving his or her arms, and controlling the bladder.

Considerable help can be given to patients with disability by means of special apparatus. Glasses can be used to help vision, and walking-frames to help patients move about by themselves. It is hoped that drugs will eventually be available to combat the disease. Discovery of its cause may lead to its prevention. D.M.H.W./J.J.F.

MUMPS (məmps′) Mumps is a virus disease. Its medical name is infectious parotitis. The infection causes pain and swelling in the glands that produce the digestive juice called saliva. The main glands that are affected are called the parotid glands. They are found in front of the ear and below the angle of the jaw. The swelling makes the face fat and distorted. Talking and chewing are difficult and painful. (The name "mumps" is said to come from the mumbling noises made by people trying to talk.) Sufferers usually take liquid food.

Mumps is probably spread by tiny droplets of moisture that people give out when they are speaking, coughing, or sneezing. The virus in the droplets settles in the mouth and nose of anyone who breathes them in. The virus enters the body and grows. It spreads through the whole body, not just in the salivary glands. The signs of illness may not appear until 18 to 24 days after the disease has been caught. This is called the incubation period. Then the patient develops a high temperature. There may be headache, a sore throat, and aching neck muscles. The salivary glands become tender and swollen. After about four days, the temperature returns to normal. After a week or ten days, the swelling of the glands disappears.

Very rarely, the disease affects other organs. The testes in men may be affected, and the ovaries in women. Normally, no damage is done to them. Very rarely, too, the membranes of the brain may become inflamed (meningitis). In children, mumps is a mild disease, although painful. Protection against the disease can be given by vaccines. *See also* VIRUS. D.M.H.W./J.J.F.

MUSCLE

Muscle (məs′ əl) is the meaty tissue with which an animal can move its body. After receiving a signal from a nerve, the muscle gets shorter, or contracts. Many muscles are attached to bones. As muscle contracts, it pulls on the bone to which it is attached. This moves the bone into a new position. It also changes the shape of the animal's body. These changes in shape help the animal move from place to place.

In the human body there are more than 600 muscles. Muscles make up about 40% of a person's body weight. Muscles do many important things. Muscles in our legs help us walk, run, and jump. Muscles in our arms help us write and hold things. Muscles in our chest let us breathe in and out. Powerful muscles in our heart work all the time, pumping blood throughout the body. Food is pushed

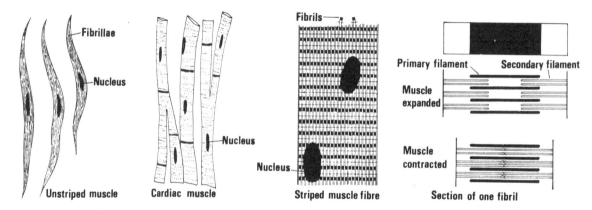

Fibrillae — Nucleus — Unstriped muscle

Cardiac muscle — Nucleus

Fibrils — Nucleus — Striped muscle fibre

Primary filament — Secondary filament — Muscle expanded — Muscle contracted — Section of one fibril

through our alimentary canal by the action of muscles. Even the size of the pupil of the eye is controlled by muscles.

The different kinds of muscle in the body There are three different kinds of muscle in the body: striated, smooth, and cardiac. Striated, or voluntary, muscle is under conscious control. Our arms and legs are moved by striated muscles. Most striated muscles are attached to bones and are sometimes called skeletal muscles. Striated muscles are made up of many fibers, each of which has small, dark stripes, or bands. Striated muscles can contract quickly and powerfully. They tire easily, however, and must rest before contracting again.

A smooth, or involuntary, muscle is also made up of fibers. However, there are no stripes or bands in these fibers. The fibers in smooth muscles are smaller than those in striated muscles. Each fiber has only one nucleus and is shaped like a cigar. Smooth muscle usually takes a longer time to contract than does striated muscle. It can also stay contracted for a very long time because it does not tire easily. The walls of the stomach and intestines are made up of smooth muscle. When this muscle contracts, it not only squeezes food through the stomach and intestine but also helps break up the food. There are smooth muscles in the walls of blood vessels. (*See* ARTERY.) These help the blood circulate throughout the body. Smooth muscles are not

Fibers of smooth muscle, cardiac muscle and striated muscle. A section of one fiber of striated muscle shows how the arrangement of the primary and secondary filaments causes the striated appearance. When the muscle contracts, the secondary filaments are drawn toward each other. The white bands become narrower.

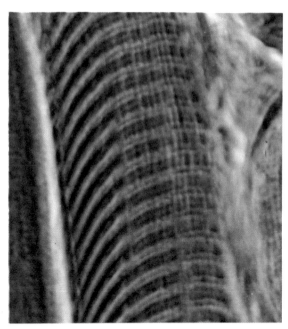

This photomicrograph (above) of a skeletal muscle fiber shows the striped appearance common in striated muscles.

under conscious control. Instead, they are controlled automatically by the autonomic nervous system. (*See* NERVOUS SYSTEM.)

The third type of muscle, cardiac muscle, is found in the heart. Like striated muscle, it has fibers which can contract powerfully and rapidly. Like smooth muscle, it is controlled automatically and does not tire easily. Cardiac fibers are branched and interconnected. As a result, the heart is like one large cell with millions of nuclei. The fibers all work together so the heart beats powerfully and rhythmically. Cardiac muscle is the only kind of muscle that continues contracting even if removed from the body. (*See* HEART.)

Sphincter muscles are special muscles that form a ring around a tube inside an animal's body. They may be either voluntary or involuntary. When a sphincter muscle contracts, it pinches off, or closes, the tube. When it relaxes, the tube is opened. The pyloric sphincter, for example, controls the passage of food from the stomach into the small intestine. (*See* STOMACH.)

Striated muscles and what they do
Striated muscles are cigar-shaped: thick in the middle and thin at the ends. Each muscle is made up of millions of fibers, or myofibrils. These fibers vary in length from less than 1 mm [0.04 in] to more than 5 mm [0.2 in]. Each fiber is a single cell with many nuclei. (*See* CELL.) Many muscle fibers are packed together to form a single bundle. A single muscle contains many bundles. The muscle is covered with a tough material called connective tissue to keep all the bundles tied together. At both ends of the muscle, the connective tissue is stretched out to form a tendon. Tendons connect the muscles to the bones.

Bones do not move by themselves. They move when the muscles contract. When a muscle contracts it pulls on the bone to which it is attached. The part of the muscle that is attached to an unmoving bone is called the origin. The part attached to the bone that moves is the insertion. This causes movements at the connections between bones. (*See* JOINT.) It may be a bending, turning, or twisting movement.

Muscles are not able to push. They can only pull. They only do work when they contract. Two of the muscles in the upper arm are the biceps and the triceps. When the biceps contracts, the arm bends. The biceps, however, cannot straighten the arm. The triceps has to do this. When the triceps contracts, it straightens the arm. Muscles work in pairs. One muscle in the pair moves a bone. The other muscle in the pair returns the bone to its normal position. These pairs are called antagonistic muscles.

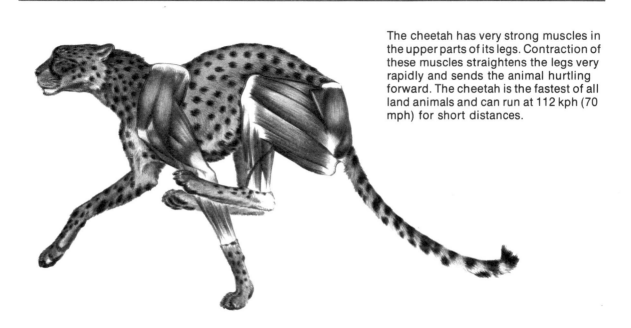

The cheetah has very strong muscles in the upper parts of its legs. Contraction of these muscles straightens the legs very rapidly and sends the animal hurtling forward. The cheetah is the fastest of all land animals and can run at 112 kph (70 mph) for short distances.

Muscle coordination All the movements that the body makes are smooth and steady. The movements are carefully controlled by nerve reflexes and the brain. (*See* BRAIN; RE-FLEX.) The instructions that make the muscles of the body work come from a part of the brain called the motor cortex. Another part of the brain called the cerebellum makes sure that all the muscles work together smoothly. When you take a book down from a shelf, many muscles in the arm and body need to work together to carry out this simple action. The cerebellum gets all these muscles working at precisely the right time.

The brain must get continuous information about the position of every muscle in the body. It would not be able to control all the body's movements without this information. Tiny sensitive devices in the muscles send signals to the brain. These signals tell the brain exactly where each muscle is. They also let the brain know how much each muscle is being stretched. (*See* PROPRIOCEPTION.) The brain can then send out the proper instructions to the muscles.

How muscles work The many tiny fibers that make up a muscle contract when they receive a signal from a nerve. Muscle fibers work in an all-or-nothing fashion. They either contract completely or not at all. When only a few of its fibers contract, the muscle shows a weak contraction. The muscle contracts more powerfully when more of its fibers contract.

Laboratory experiments have helped show how muscles work. Tiny electrical wires were attached to a muscle. When an electric current was passed through a wire, the muscle contracted. This showed that the signals a muscle receives from a nerve are very much like electricity. The muscles in our body, however, do not contract by electricity alone. The fibers contract in the presence of a special chemical called acetylcholine. A nerve divides into many fine branches before it reaches a muscle. A signal from the brain travels along this nerve until it reaches these tiny nerve endings. (*See* NERVE CELL.) As soon as a nerve ending receives a signal it releases acetylcholine, causing the muscle fiber to contract.

Each muscle fiber is made up of many millions of tiny threads, or filaments. There are two kinds of filament. There are short thick filaments made of a protein called myosin. There are also thinner filaments made of a protein called actin. The thick myosin filaments are sandwiched between the thin actin filaments. The actin filaments are able to slide over the myosin filaments. When a single muscle fiber contracts, all the actin filaments start sliding over the myosin filaments until the ends of the actin filaments meet. When a muscle fiber expands, the actin filaments slide out from the rows of myosin filaments. A chemical called ATP gives the filaments the energy they need to slide over each other. (*See* ATP.)

When a muscle contracts, it produces a waste product called lactic acid. If a person is exercising very hard, lactic acid may build up in the muscles. This causes the muscles to tire, a condition called muscle fatigue. Rapidly contracting muscles use oxygen faster than the body can supply it and lactic acid is formed when the oxygen supply is insufficient. Before the muscle can contract at full strength again, it must rest so that the lactic acid can be broken down and removed. Often, someone with muscle fatigue breathes heavily. This helps meet his oxygen debt, or the need for oxygen in his muscles. *See also* ANATOMY.   J.A./J.J.F.

MUSHROOM (mǝsh′ rǝm) Mushrooms are a widely known variety of plants called fungi. Mushrooms grow in decaying vegetable matter and are sometimes found under leaves or moss.

Botanists do not separate mushrooms and toadstools into two different groups. People generally think of mushrooms as being edi-

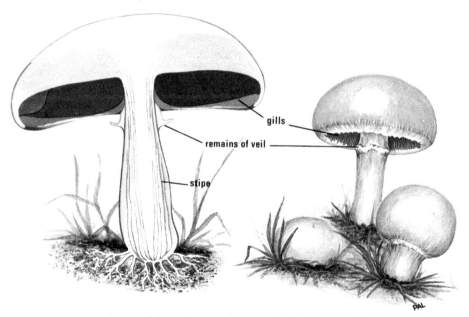

Mushrooms are commonly found in soil where the mycelium of the fungus can grow. From the button stage of early development, mushrooms grow until their undersides break open and expose the gills—which contain the spores in the basidia.

ble, while the term "toadstool" refers to mushrooms that are poisonous. Only an expert can tell which mushrooms are safe to eat and which contain deadly poisons.

There are more than 35,000 different types of mushrooms. The different types have many different shapes. Some look like umbrellas. Others may look like a stack of shelves. Mushrooms come in many different colors, such as various shades of white, pink, lavender, yellow, orange, red, gray, and brown.

The mushroom grows underground as a thread-like mycelium. The mycelium looks like a web of threads, sometimes packed together like a mass of felt. At suitable times, a round body shape called a cap (sporophore) is formed. This is pushed out of the ground on a thick stalk. The underside of the cap breaks open and expands, revealing a number of radiating gills. The basidia lie between the gills, which darken as the spores ripen and fall. (*See* BASIDIUM.)

Human beings have eaten mushrooms since early times. Mushrooms are now grown on a large scale in special, darkened sheds with carefully controlled humidity, ventilation, and temperature. In most countries, mushrooms are considered a delicacy rather than a main food. *See also* FUNGUS.

J.J.A./M.H.S.

MUSKELLUNGE (məs′ kə lənj′) A muskellunge is a large, freshwater fish that belongs to the pike family Esocidae. It is found in a relatively small area from southern Canada to Tennessee. The muskellunge, also called the muskie, is one of the largest freshwater fishes. The largest reported muskie was 46 kg [102 lb]. The present fishing record is 31 kg [69 lb] and 163.8 cm [64.5 in] long. The muskie is a popular gamefish.

The muskellunge lives in weedy lakes and slow-moving rivers. It feeds almost exclusively on other fish. It has been known to take mice, squirrels, ducks, and just about anything else it can fit into its mouth. *See also* PIKE. S.R.G./E.C.M.

MUSK OX (məs′ käks′) The musk ox (*Ovibos moschatus*) is a shaggy-haired mammal of the family Bovidae. Musk oxen live in northern Canada and Greenland, where temperatures fall to −50°C [−58°F]. A few musk oxen have been introduced onto several islands off the coast of Alaska.

The musk ox has a large head, short neck, and short legs. It has a musky odor. Bulls (males) stand about 1.5 m [5 ft] at the shoulder. They weigh about 400 kg [880 lb]. The cows (females) are smaller. In males, the sharply curved horns grow from the center and form a thick, bony plate across the forehead. Females and young have smaller horns. The musk ox has a very thick, woolly undercoat to keep it warm. This undercoat is overlaid by long brown or black hairs, which reach down close to the ground on each side of the animal.

Musk oxen feed on grass and low-growing plants such as lichens and willows. Musk oxen are sometimes preyed on by Arctic wolves. When attacked, musk oxen form a circle with the young inside. The larger animals present a front of horns facing outward. Few wolves can get through such a defense. But this method of defense is very poor when musk oxen are faced by human hunters, who can shoot them easily. J.J.A./J.J.M.

Adult musk ox bulls are about 1.5 m [5 ft] tall and 2.4 m [8 ft] long. They use their sharp, curved horns as a defense against wolves.

MUSKRAT (məs′ krat′) The muskrat (*Ondatra zibethica*) is a rodent found in many parts of North America and in parts of Europe. Muskrats are so called because of their strong, musklike odor. The animals live in swampy places near streams and rivers.

Muskrats spend a lot of time in the water. They have scaly, vertically flattened tails by which they steer in the water. The webbed toes on their hind feet help them to swim. Muskrats grow about 30 cm [1 ft] in length, not including their long tail.

Most muskrats make tunnels in the banks of streams. The animals live in the tunnels. Muskrats also make "houses" by plastering plants together with mud. These houses often have entrances above and below water. Muskrats feed on green vegetation, berries, twigs, snails, and the meat from dead animals.

Female muskrats usually give birth to two or three litters each year. Each litter often consists of three to eight young. As a result, the muskrat population increases rapidly. They can often overcrowd an area.

The muskrat has a coat of long, shiny hair. Muskrat fur makes warm coats. The fur is often dyed to look like mink or sable. Muskrat meat is sold as "marsh rabbit."

J.J.A./J.J.M.

MUSSEL (məs′ əl) A mussel is a bivalve that lives in salt or fresh water. It is in the phylum Mollusca. Sea mussels belong to the family Mytilidae. Fresh water mussels are in the family Unionidae. The common mussel's body is covered with a protective shell made up of two pieces called valves. The valves are hinged at one point and can be opened and closed somewhat like a book. The mussel's body lies inside the shell. It consists of various organs, including the foot, gills, stomach, and heart.

Several kinds of sea mussels can be eaten. The common blue mussel, which is from 8 to 15 cm [3 to 6 in] long, is a popular food in Europe. Its shell is bluish black on the outside

Mussels draw in water, which contains tiny particles of food, through their frilled inhalent siphons. After food has been filtered out, the water is driven out through the exhalent siphon

and pearly blue on the inside. Sea mussels use the foot to spin long, silky threads called a byssus. The byssus anchors the mussel to a rock or other object where it may spend the rest of its life.

Mussels usually gather in large numbers, covering rocks, pier legs, and any other solid object. They can survive a high degree of pollution, and are often found in and around estuaries and harbors.

Freshwater mussels are a valuable source of mother-of-pearl, which lines the inside of their shells. Mother-of-pearl is used to make pearl buttons. W.R.P./C.S.H.

MUSTARD FAMILY The mustard (məs′ tərd) family includes about 1,500 species of plants, most of which are herbaceous annuals native to temperate areas of the world. They are dicotyledons and have large, thick, dark green leaves with divided margins. The flowers are usually yellow and have four sepals and four petals arranged like a cross. There are six stamens, two of which are usually shorter than the others.

Members of the genus *Brassica* include cabbage, turnips, and mustard. Black mustard (*Brassica nigra*) grows to a height of 2 m [6.6 ft] or more. Its dark brown seeds are used in most commercial mustard products. White mustard (*Brassica hirta*) grows to a height of 90 cm [3 ft] and produces white seeds used as a garnish in salads. A third type of mustard, *Brassica juncea,* is grown for its leaves which can be cooked and eaten as greens. Mustard seeds contain an oil which is used as a spice, as a medicine, or in mustard plasters used for pain relief. Other members of this family include horseradish and wallflowers. *See also* BRASSICA. A.J.C./M.H.S.

Charlock (*Brassica kaber*), a member of the mustard family, is shown above. The yellow-flowered weed is often troublesome in grainfields. It grows in temperate areas.

MUTATION (myü tā′ shən) A mutation is a change in an inherited characteristic that is caused by a change in a gene. (*See* GENE.) As the result of a mutation, an offspring inherits a characteristic that was not present in either of the parents. This new characteristic is part of the offspring's genetic code and will be passed on to future generations.

An organism that has undergone a mutation is called a mutant. Most mutations are harmful to the organism, often causing its death before it is able to reproduce and pass on the mutated gene. Some mutations, however, are helpful. Mutations are an important part of the process of evolution. (*See* EVOLUTION.)

A mutation is either spontaneous or induced. A spontaneous mutation is a random accident that disturbs the normal structure of DNA in a gene. An induced mutation is externally caused by such factors as drugs, X rays, or other types of radiation. *See also* GENETICS; HEREDITY. A.J.C./E.R.L.

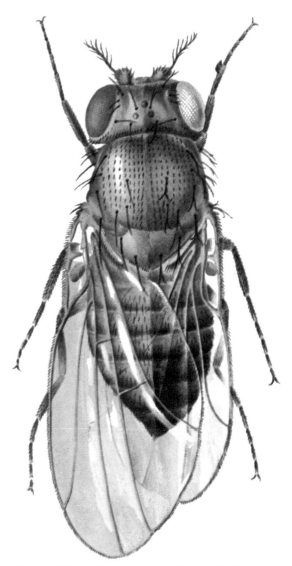

A *Drosophila melanogaster*, a kind of fruit fly, is shown above. Mutation causes the cells of the fly's larva to develop into a red-eyed female on the left side of the body, and a white-eyed male on the right side. The normal condition for these flies is red eyes and large wings. Mutation caused the white eye and small wing in this fly.

MYCORRHIZA *See* FUNGUS.

MYNA (mī′ nə) Myna is the name given to several types of birds in the starling family. Myna birds are found in Burma, India, and other parts of Asia. These birds are usually quite social. They often build nests in cracks and various other parts of buildings. Myna birds are sometimes seen among chickens or perched on the backs of cattle. Mynas feed on fruits, insects, and worms.

The common house myna (*Acridotheres tristis*) is slightly larger than the American robin. This species has handsome coloring, ranging from reddish brown on the lower breast to deep black on the upper breast, neck, and head. The house myna's bill and legs are a bright yellow. The crested myna (*Acridotheres cristatellus*) lives in cultivated fields and pastures. This bird is often found living among human beings. The talking myna (*Gracula religiosa*) is often kept as a pet. J.J.A./L.L.S.

MYRIAPOD (mir′ ē ə päd′) Myriapod is the name given to animals with many legs, such as centipedes and millipedes. It is not a scientific name, but it is a very descriptive name. Myriapod means ''many feet.''

W.R.P./C.S.H.

MYRTLE FAMILY The myrtle (mərt′ əl) family (Myrtaceae) includes about 3,000 species of evergreen trees and shrubs that grow in tropical and subtropical regions. They have simple, opposite leaves. (*See* LEAF.) Their flowers are often large and ornate with four or five overlapping sepals, four or five petals, and many stamens.

Members of the myrtle family include the bayberry, clove, and eucalyptus. The myrtles (genus *Myrtus*) include about 100 species, some of which produce edible berries. The leaves of the common myrtle (*Myrtus communis*) are used to make perfume.

J.M.C./M.H.S.

NAIL (nāl) Nails are hard growths from the hands or feet of vertebrate animals. Human beings, monkeys, and apes all have flattened nails at the ends of their fingers. Many other animals, such as birds, have sharp claws. Other animals, such as horses, have blunt hooves.

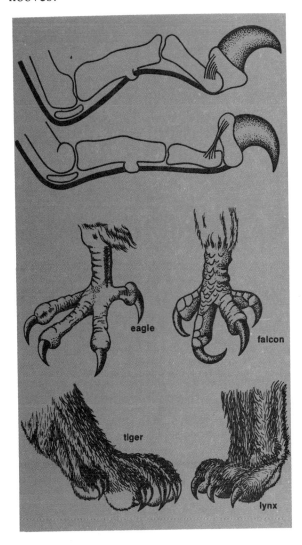

The cat's claw (top) is retracted by a muscle in the toe. When the claw is extended, a muscle in the leg contracts, pulling on a tendon on the underside of the foot. The claws of an eagle, a falcon, a tiger, and a lynx are shown above. Nails and claws often serve as weapons.

All these growths are similar structures formed from the outer layer of the skin, the epidermis. The growths consist of hardened skin cells. They contain a hard material called keratin, which also forms animals' horns. Deer antlers are another kind of growth. The skin below the nail is called the matrix. Near the root of the nail, the cells are smaller. They carry less blood. The white, circular spot containing these cells is the lunula. If a nail is torn off, it will grow again, as long as the matrix has not been totally injured. The state of a person's health is often indicated by the nails. Illness often affects their growth.

All nails, claws, and hooves have certain functions, such as serving as weapons.

J.J.A./J.J.F.

NAPHTHALENE (naf′ thə lēn′) Naphthalene ($C_{10}H_8$) is a white crystalline solid with a smell of mothballs. The crystals melt at 80°C [176°F]. A molecule of naphthalene consists of two benzene molecules joined together along one side. (*See* BENZENE.)

Most naphthalene is used to make dyes and plastics. The smell of naphthalene repels insects and is used to keep clothes free of moths. It is also used in pesticides in the garden. It helps to keep the soil and plants free of pests.

M.E./J.M.

NAPIER, JOHN (1550–1617) John Napier (nā′ pē ər) was born in Scotland. He wrote books on religion and studied mathematics as a hobby. He is best known for his invention of logarithms. (*See* LOGARITHM.) By using logarithms, complicated numbers can be easily multiplied or divided. The logarithm of a number is found from lists of tables called logarithm tables. If two numbers are to be multiplied, their logarithms are added. If they are to be divided, their logarithms are subtracted from each other. Most logarithm tables have a base 10. With that base, log 10 is 1, log 100 is 2, and so on. Scientists and mathematicians frequently use a base *e*. The number *e* is approximately 2.718. These logarithms are named after John Napier. They are called Napierian logarithms. Napier also invented other devices to make calculations easier. He invented an early form of slide rule now called Napier's bones. (*See* SLIDE RULE.)

M.E./D.G.F.

NARCISSUS (när sis′ əs) Narcissus is a genus of about 40 species of flowering plants belonging to the amaryllis family. They are native to Europe and Asia and are cultivated worldwide for their beautiful, fragrant flowers. They grow from poisonous brown bulbs. (*See* BULB AND CORM.) A single white, yellow, or pink flower grows at the end of a tall stalk which rises above the sword-shaped leaves. The flower has six petals surrounding a trumpet-shaped tube. Two popular species are the daffodil (*Narcissus pseudo-narcissus*) and the poet's narcissus (*Narcissus poeticus.*)

The name "narcissus" comes from Greek mythology. According to the myth, Narcissus was the son of a god. He was so selfish and so proud of his good looks that the other gods decided to punish him. They made him fall in love with his own reflection in a pond. Narcissus was so in love that he refused to leave his reflection for even a minute. When he died, the gods turned him into a flower—the narcissus. *See also* AMARYLLIS FAMILY; DAFFODIL.

A.J.C./M.H.S.

NARCOTIC (när kät′ ik) Narcotics are a group of drugs. In the United States, the word usually means any addictive drug. Doctors use the word narcotics for drugs that deaden pain and cause sleepiness. An important narcotic is opium. Morphine and heroin, two other important narcotics, can be obtained from opium. These drugs block the part of the brain that makes us aware of pain. Morphine is commonly used as a powerful painkiller. (*See* ANALGESIC.) Opium, morphine, and heroin are all highly addictive.

M.E./J.F.

NARWHAL (när′ wäl′) The narwhal (*Monodon monoceros*) is a grayish white, dark-spotted whale found in the Arctic Ocean. The male is noted for its spiral ivory tusk, which is about 2.4 m [8 ft] in length and grows in a counterclockwise spiral. This tusk sticks out of the left side of the male's head. The tusk is the narwhal's only tooth. Very rarely, a narwhal may have two tusks. Females are usually without tusks. However, when they have tusks, they almost always have two of them. How the narwhal uses its tusk is not known. But the tusks of most adult narwhals are worn at the tip, indicating some kind of usage.

Narwhals grow about 5.5 m [18 ft] in length, not including the tusk. The animals may weigh up to 1.8 metric tons [2 tons]. Narwhals feed mainly on soft squids and cuttlefish. Some Eskimos hunt these whales. The skin is eaten. The tusks are made into tools. *See also* WHALE.   J.J.A./J.J.M.

NASA NASA (National Aeronautics and Space Administration) is the government agency that runs the United States space program. NASA was established in 1958 and is headquartered in Washington, D.C.

NASA employs about 24,000 people in its many installations across the country. The John F. Kennedy Space Center at Cape Canaveral, Florida, is where most spacecraft are launched. The Johnson Space Center in Houston, Texas, is the control center for manned space flights. Satellites and space probes are monitored from the Goddard Space Flight Center in Maryland. NASA operates several other research and development facilities in various parts of the country. *See also* SPACE TRAVEL.   J.M.C./C.R.

NASTURTIUM (nə stər′ shəm) Nasturtium is the name given to plants of genus

NASA has been involved in the United States' space travel activities for more than twenty-five years.

Tropaeolum. They are native to Central and South America. Common nasturtium (*Tropaeolum majus*) is a climbing plant that grows to a length of about 3 m [10 ft]. Its flowers are yellowish orange with red spots. Each flower has five sepals, three of which form a nectar-containing tube called a spur. There are also five petals. The leaves have a peppery taste and are sometimes used in salads.

Nasturtium is also a genus in the mustard family. (*See* MUSTARD FAMILY.) It includes several aquatic herbaceous plants such as watercress. A.J.C./M.H.S.

NATIONAL PARK (nash′ nəl pärk) A national park is land that has been acquired by the federal government for the purpose of recreation and conserving wildlife, natural resources, and beautiful scenery. (*See* CONSERVATION; NATURAL RESOURCE.) The first national park in the United States was created in 1872. Yellowstone National Park, located in Wyoming, was founded in that year in order to protect many species of animals that were becoming rare. Today, Yellowstone has more grizzly bears than most places in the lower United States. (*See* GRIZZLY BEAR.) The park also contains springs of boiling water, geysers that shoot water hundreds of feet into the air, and beautiful waterfalls. If the park had not been established, the bears might have been killed as they were in other parts, the springs drained, and the waterfalls dammed. Yellowstone National Park, like other national parks, makes sure that these natural wonders are protected for everyone to enjoy. Every year, thousands of people visit and camp in the park.

More than 341,360 sq km (131,800 sq mi) of land, an area larger than Missouri and Iowa combined, is now in national parks in the United States. The parks include seashores, mountains, prairies, rivers, deserts, and forests. Many species of plants and animals are protected in these parks. The idea of national parks has spread to other countries, too. There are now many national parks all over the world. Africa has huge parks where antelope, giraffes, elephants, lions, and baboons roam freely.

Scientists often use national parks to study plants and animals in their natural setting. The parks also earn much money. Restaurants, motels, and gas stations are built to serve the thousands of visitors. Local residents earn money from these businesses. Many states in the United States now have state parks. Provinces in Canada have established provincial parks. These parks are similar to the national parks except that they are owned by the state and provincial governments instead of the federal government. *See also* ECOSYSTEM; ENVIRONMENT. S.R.G./R.J.B.

NATURAL RESOURCE (nach′ rəl rē′ sȯrs′) A natural resource is a valuable product or property that exists in nature. People do not make natural resources, but often collect them to use them. Trees, gas, oil, water, and soil are all natural resources. Some resources are renewable. This means that when part of the resource is used, it is replaced. Trees are a renewable natural resource because when they are chopped down, more grow in their place. Oil is a non-renewable natural resource because there is only so much oil underground. When that oil is gone, there will be no more. We now realize that we cannot afford to waste non-renewable natural resources.

Different areas have different natural resources. The state of Oregon has many trees. The state of Maine has a lot of seafood off its coast. Illinois has very good soil for crops. California and Florida have warm weather that is excellent for fruits and vegetables. All of these things are valuable natural resources. *See also* CONSERVATION; ECOSYSTEM; NATIONAL PARK. S.R.G./R.J.B.

NAUTILOID (nȯt′ əl ȯid′) A nautiloid is a marine cephalopod with a straight or coiled shell into which it can retract its muscular tentacles. Although fossils show that there have been nautiloids for more than 500 million years, only three of more than 2,000 species are still in existence. These primitive molluscs may live as deep as 200 m [660 ft] in the Indian and western Pacific Oceans. *See also* CEPHALOPOD; MOLLUSCA. A.J.C./C.S.H.

NAVIGATION

Navigation (nav′ ə gā′ shən) is the science of finding the position and directing the movement of a craft from one point to another. The word navigate comes from two Latin words—*navis,* meaning ship, and *agere,* meaning to direct. All navigators, whether on land, sea, in the air or in space, have to find their position and work out the direction in which they want to travel.

A brief history Early sea navigators sailed without instruments. They moved chiefly from point to point along coasts, always trying to keep within sight of land. It was very dangerous to go out into the open sea.

The invention of the astrolabe was a tremendous help to early navigators. The astrolabe made it possible for the navigator to measure roughly the angle between the horizon and heavenly bodies. (*See* ASTROLABE.)

Sometime around 1000–1200 A.D. the magnetic compass was being used by Chinese and Mediterranean sailors. By using the compass, navigators could set a course for the direction in which they wished to go.

In the 1700s, the invention of the accurate chronometer (to tell time) and the sextant (to measure angles) made it possible for navigators to know exactly where they were, even when far from land. (*See* CHRONOMETER.)

Methods and instruments Navigators on ships and aircraft often use algebra, geometry, and trigonometry to find out where they are in relation to landmarks and stars. Various navigational aids and instruments are used to get information about time, direction, distance, speed, and position. The techniques of navigation are piloting, dead reckoning, celestial navigation, and electronic navigation. All these methods are commonly used in combination with each other. Piloting is simply a means of navigating by watching out for landmarks. Ship navigators use piloting when close to land. They watch for lighthouses, buoys, and other landmarks. An air navigator may check his position by using such landmarks as rivers and bridges. Piloting is called "contact flying" by airplane pilots.

Dead reckoning is a way of figuring courses and distances from a known position by marking the ship's course and speed on a chart. A chart is a carefully prepared map which helps the navigator find his position. A navigator uses dead reckoning when he wants a good guess of his position. For example, a ship leaves New York Bay at 2 P.M. The ship's course is east. Its speed is 32.2 km [20 mi] per hour. At 5 P.M., the navigator checks the direction of the ship's course, how long the ship has been sailing, and its speed. Then he may reckon (guess) that the ship is 96.5 km [60 mi] east of New York. This may not be exact. But dead reckoning is accurate enough for many purposes.

Celestial navigation is a way to check a position by observing the sun, moon, stars, and planets. Celestial navigation makes use of the fact that the sun and stars are always in certain positions depending on the time of day (or night) and the date of the year. To navigate by the sun or stars, a navigator uses a sextant. A sextant measures the angle between the sun (or a star) and the horizon. When the navigator knows this angle, he looks up the sun or star in a book of tables called the *American Ephemeris and Nautical Almanac.*

This book gives the exact position of each heavenly body for exact times and dates. From the sun angle, plus the date and time, the navigator calculates his approximate position. By measuring the sun at two times several hours apart, he can get an exact position.

Navigators today use several radio and radar systems to aid in finding their position. Electronic navigation makes use of such electronic devices as voice and code radio, radio direction finders, loran, shoran, radar, electronic depth finders, and communications satellites. One system that airplanes use consists of radio signals broadcast from special towers at airports. When the pilot is on the airway, he hears a special hum. If he goes off course, he hears a series of beeps. Another system is called loran, which stands for "long range navigation." Ocean-crossing airplanes use loran. Two radar units several kilometers or miles apart on land send a signal out to sea. The signals show up as two dots of light on the airplane's radar screen. The navigator turns a dial until the two dots become one, showing the airplane's position. A more recent system makes use of earth-orbiting satellites. Each satellite has a radio transmitter. The navigator tunes in the "beep" from a satellite. He then uses a special computer to measure the angle between the satellite and the ship or plane. The computer then figures out the position of the ship or plane.

Astronauts also have a problem knowing where they are. When a ship sails the ocean or a jet plane crosses the sky, the place the ship started from and the place it is going to do not move around with relation to each other. But when astronauts blast off for the moon, the earth and the moon are both moving. In order for astronauts to find their way to and back

A mariner's astrolabe, made in 1585, is pictured in front of an ancient navigational map. Before the sextant was invented, the astrolabe was used to observe the position of celestial bodies.

The azimuth compass (above) was made about 1720.

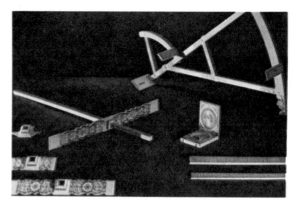

A set of ivory navigational instruments, made about 1700, are shown. The sundial was made in 1660.

from the moon, they have a special sextant telescope aboard the spacecraft. This instrument measures the angle between the earth and a star, and then gives this information to a computer. The computer works out the spacecraft's position.

Scientists who are looking ahead to the building of spaceships for travel from the earth to other planets have worked out the problem of navigating in the solar system. Space navigation is called astrogation. The navigator, called an astrogator, would need a special almanac with tables giving the positions of planets in relation to the sun at any time. The astrogator would measure the angle between the sun and the two closest planets. He would then compute his distance from the sun by using geometry. (*See* SPACE TRAVEL.)

Getting from here to there Knowing the position of his craft is the first half of a navigator's job. The second half concerns getting the craft where it is supposed to go. For an idea of how this happens, the following is a brief description of a voyage on a ship.

First, the navigator must make sure that

John Harrison (left) invented the chronometer, which enabled navigators to find longitude more accurately than had previously been possible.

all the necessary tools, aids, and instruments are aboard. Once the ship leaves the harbor, the navigator finds out the ship's position and the exact time. This position is called the point of departure. For example, the point of departure may be the time when a ship passes a buoy. The navigator, noting the time, marks a small circle on the chart.

The navigator then uses his chart to plot a course. A network of imaginary lines is on each chart. Lines of longitude run north-south. Lines of latitude run east-west. Each point on the earth has its own position in terms of latitude and longitude. (*See* LATITUDE AND LONGITUDE.) Knowing his position, the navigator draws a line from that spot to the spot he wants to go. This line is his course. The course is seldom a straight line. Ships must avoid storms and sail around islands. At every planned change of course, the navigator must measure his new position and set a new course. The navigator must have training in meteorology (weather science) and be able to read weather instruments. The navigator also keeps a close check on the depth of the water. He takes these soundings with an instrument called a fathometer. From time to time during the voyage, the navigator uses all four basic methods of navigation.

A landfall is the first land sighted after a voyage. The navigator checks the landfall on his chart to make sure his navigation has been accurate. Again, the navigator, using the fathometer, keeps a close check on the depth of the water to avoid going aground as the ship enters the harbor. J.J.A./R.W.L.

Lighthouses serve both as beacons—to warn ships of navigational hazards, such as rocks—and as landmarks, by which sailors can tell their position. Each lighthouse has its own characteristic light and sound signal.

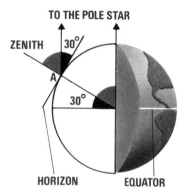

In the nothern hemisphere, latitude can be found by measuring the angle of the pole star above the horizon. In this diagram, the angle (in black), representing latitude, is the same as the angle made by the horizon point and the equator.

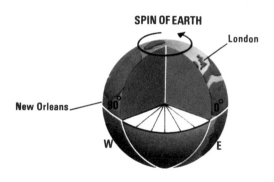

Longitude is most easily measured by time, because every 15° of longitude represents 1 hour of time. If the local time in New Orleans is 18.00 and the time in London (Greenwich mean time) is midnight, the difference is 6 hours or 90° of longitude.

NEANDERTHAL (nē an' dər thȯl') Neanderthal people were primitive human beings. They lived during the late Pleistocene epoch, from 35,000 to 100,000 years ago. Neanderthal people are named for the Neander Gorge in Germany, where their fossils were first discovered in 1856. Neanderthal people are considered to be an early form of *Homo sapiens*.

Neanderthal people stood about 157 cm [5 ft 2 in], and walked erect. They had powerful bones and strong teeth. Their brains were equivalent in size to the brains of modern people.

Fossils of Neanderthal people have been found in Europe, Asia, and Africa. Primitive tools and animal bones were discovered near the European site, supporting the theory that Neanderthal people were hunters. Neanderthal people probably lived in makeshift shelters and caves. *See also* PLEISTOCENE EPOCH.

J.M.C./S.O.

NEBULA (neb' yə lə) A nebula is a large cloud of gases and dust in outer space. The name nebula comes from the Latin word meaning cloud. There are two main types of nebulae: diffuse nebulae and planetary nebulae.

Diffuse nebulae are much larger than planetary nebulae. Sometimes, a diffuse nebula is close enough to a star so that dust in the nebula reflects the starlight. This type of nebula is called a reflective nebula.

A diffuse nebula is sometimes energized by a nearby powerful star. When this occurs, the nebula begins to emit its own radiation. Such a nebula is called an emission nebula. An emission nebula may be a star in its formative stages.

Diffuse nebulae may occur in a region of outer space where there are no nearby stars. The dust in the nebula may actually block out or obscure the stars behind it. This type of diffuse nebula is called a dark nebula.

A planetary nebula is an expanding cloud of glowing gas that surrounds a star. No one is sure where they come from. *See also* MAGNITUDE; STAR.

J.M.C./C.R.

The Crab nebula is a mass of glowing gas produced when a star exploded A.D. 1054.

The Horsehead nebula (above) consists of a dark mass of dust in the shape of a horse's head. It stands out against a bright background of stars and can be seen in the constellation of Orion.

The Great nebula (below) in the constellation of Orion can be seen as a faint patch south of Orion's belt. Bright, very hot stars within the nebula cause the gas of the nebula to glow brightly.

NECTARINE (nek′ tə rēn′) Nectarine (*Prunus persica*) is a smooth-skinned variety of peach. It is a member of the rose family.

Nectarines and peaches have identical tree and leaf characteristics. Both require the same type of soil and climate for successful cultivation.

Nectarines have a plumlike appearance because of their smooth skin. The flesh of the fruit may be red, yellow, or white. Nectarines are rich in Vitamins A and C. *See also* PEACH; ROSE FAMILY.   J.M.C./M.H.S.

NEGATIVE NUMBER (neg′ ə tiv nəm bər) When you subtract, you take one number away from another. For example, subtracting 2 from 5 leaves you with 3. This is written as 5 − 2 = 3. Suppose that the second number is bigger than the first, for example 5 − 7. 5 − 5 = 0 and 7 is 5 plus 2. Therefore 5 − 7 is 0 with 2 left over. The answer is called minus 2. It is written as 5 − 7 = −2. −2 is a negative number. Two negative numbers can be added together to give another negative number: −2 + (−3) = −5. When two negative numbers are multiplied together, they give an ordinary positive number: −2 × (−3) = +6. *See also* NUMBER.   M.E./S.P.A.

NEKTON (nek′ tən) Nekton is the name given to plants or animals that swim in the sea. Fish, whales, octopuses, tiny crusta-

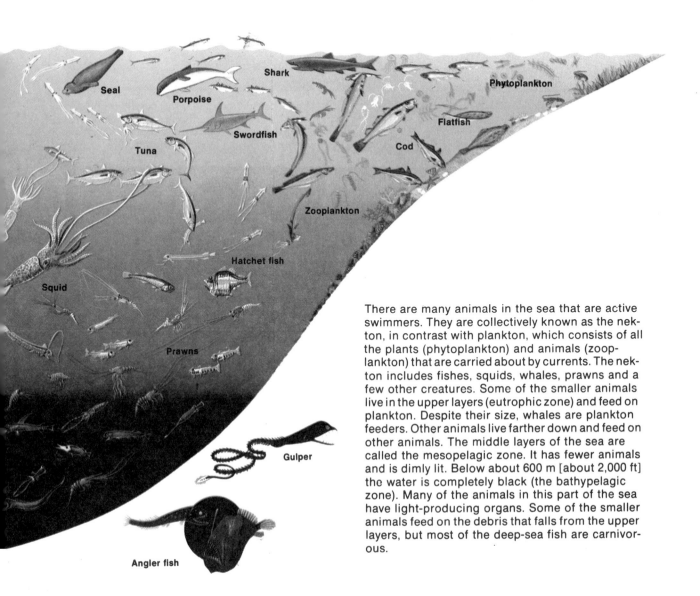

There are many animals in the sea that are active swimmers. They are collectively known as the nekton, in contrast with plankton, which consists of all the plants (phytoplankton) and animals (zooplankton) that are carried about by currents. The nekton includes fishes, squids, whales, prawns and a few other creatures. Some of the smaller animals live in the upper layers (eutrophic zone) and feed on plankton. Despite their size, whales are plankton feeders. Other animals live farther down and feed on other animals. The middle layers of the sea are called the mesopelagic zone. It has fewer animals and is dimly lit. Below about 600 m [about 2,000 ft] the water is completely black (the bathypelagic zone). Many of the animals in this part of the sea have light-producing organs. Some of the smaller animals feed on the debris that falls from the upper layers, but most of the deep-sea fish are carnivorous.

ceans, and small, swimming one-celled plants are all nekton. Organisms that do not swim but drift in the sea are called plankton. Organisms that attach themselves to the sea floor are called benthos. Some organisms are benthos at one time in their lives, plankton at another, and nekton at another time. *See also* BENTHOS; CRUSTACEAN; PLANKTON.

S.R.G./R.J.B.

NEMATODE (něm′ ə tōd′) A nematode is a slender, round worm belonging to the phylum Nematoda. Some nematodes are so small they can be seen only with a microscope. Most grow to be 1 mm to 5 cm [0.04 to 2 in] long. A nematode's body is usually pointed at both ends. Males are smaller than females.

Some nematodes live in soil and water. Many, such as the eelworm, live as parasites in plants. Hookworms, lungworms, pinworms, trichinellas, and filarias live as parasites in human beings. They also live in dogs, sheep, and horses.

Nematodes are abundant everywhere in the world, and they rival insects in their numbers.

W.R.P./C.S.H.

NEODYMIUM (nē′ ō dim′ ē əm) Neodymium (Nd) is a bright, silvery white metallic element. Its atomic number is 60 and its atomic weight is 144.24. Neodymium melts at 1,024°C [1,875°F] and boils at 3,068°C [5,554°F]. Its relative density varies between 6.8 and 7.0.

Neodymium was discovered in 1885 by the Austrian chemist Karl Auer von Welsbach. It is one of the rare earth group of metals. (*See* RARE EARTH ELEMENT.) It is found in rare earth minerals such as cerite and monazite. Many compounds of neodymium are rose colored. For this reason, its compounds are used in lasers and to color ceramics and glass.

M.E./J.R.W.

NEON (nē′ än′) Neon (Ne) is a gaseous element. It has no odor or color. Its atomic number is 10 and its atomic weight is 20.183. Neon boils at −246°C [−410.8°F] and

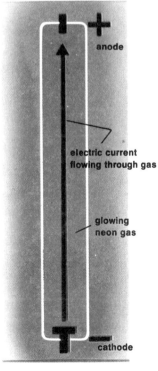

anode

electric current
flowing through gas

glowing
neon gas

cathode

When an electric current is passed through neon gas in a tube (left), the gas gives out a bright orange red glow. There is no filament wire in the tube. The current passing through the gas knocks electrons out of their orbits in the atoms of neon. The free electrons acquire energy. When they return to their orbits, energy is released as light. Adding a small quantity of mercury vapor produces a green blue light. Neon tubes may be used as signs or even as a neon sculpture like the one at the far left.

freezes at −248.7°C [−415.7°F]. Neon is one of the noble gases. (*See* NOBLE GAS.) This means that it is very unreactive. Only a few compounds of neon are known. Neon was discovered by the British chemist Sir William Ramsay in 1898.

Neon occurs in small amounts in the air. In one cubic meter [35.3 cu ft] of air there are about 18 cubic millimeters [0.7 cu in] of neon. Neon is obtained by liquefying air. The liquefied air is then allowed to boil. The neon is separated from the other gases by a process called distillation. (*See* DISTILLATION.) Most neon is used in neon advertising signs. If electricity is passed through neon, it glows a bright orange-red. If a little mercury is added, the color changes to green or blue. Neon is also used in navigation lights and beacons.

M.E./J.R.W.

NEOPRENE (nē′ ə prēn′) Sometimes called polychloroprene, neoprene is a kind of artificial rubber made from a substance called chloroprene. Large numbers of molecules of chloroprene are joined together in a chain to form one molecule of neoprene. This process is called polymerization. (*See* POLYMERIZATION.) Neoprene resists corrosion by the air better than natural rubber. It cannot be used at very low temperatures.

M.E./J.M.

NEOTENY (nē′ ə tē′ nē) Neoteny is the ability of the juvenile or larval stage of an organism to become sexually active. This means that some of an animal's juvenile or larval features persist into the adult state. This is shown by a number of salamanders, such as the axolotl. The adult in this species usually keeps the gills it used as a tadpole. A more extreme example is provided by the mud puppy, a salamander from Mexico. The mud puppy never grows up. It spends its whole life in the tadpole stage. However, it does mature sexually, and reproduces.

Neoteny may explain the link between jellylike sea squirts and the backboned ani-

mals, or vertebrates. The adult sea squirt does not look like any backboned animal, but it does have a larva that looks something like a tadpole. It is possible that some alteration in the hormones prevented the larvae from changing into adult form, but did not prevent them from breeding. This could explain how the earliest fishlike creatures might have come into existence.

W.R.P./E.R.L.

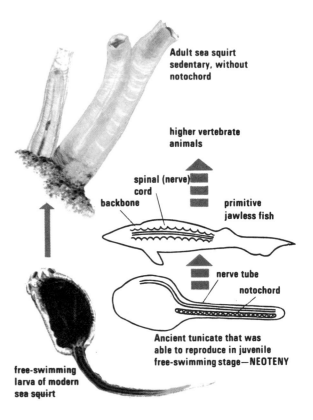

It's possible that early fish may have evolved from a neotenous form of a sea-squirt larva—which loses its notochord and nerve tube as an adult. If the larva did not develop to adult form, but was capable of reproducing, fish may have resulted.

The adult mud puppy has several larval features which show neotony. It has external gills, weak legs, and a powerful, flat tail.

NEPTUNE (nep′ tün′) Neptune is the eighth planet from the sun. It is named for the Roman sea god Neptune. Neptune and Pluto are the only known planets of the solar system that cannot be seen by the unaided eye.

Neptune has a diameter of 49,500 km [30,760 mi]. The planet orbits the sun every 165 years, following an elliptical (oval-shaped) path. Its orbit averages about 4,498 million km [2,795 million mi] from the sun. Neptune makes one complete rotation on its axis every 15 hours and 40 minutes.

Neptune has an atmosphere composed of hydrogen, methane, helium, and ammonia. Thick clouds of frozen gases and ice are visible through a telescope. The methane in Neptune's atmosphere gives the planet a greenish appearance.

Astronomers know very little about the surface of Neptune. Neptune has seasons caused by the 30° tilt of its axis. The planet has extremely low temperatures, probably below −173°C [−280°F]. The lack of oxygen and the cold temperatures make earth-type life on Neptune unlikely. (*See* EXOBIOLOGY.) Neptune has two satellites, Triton and Nereid, and is encircled by two rings. Triton orbits Neptune every six days, following a circular path. It has a diameter of about 4,800 km [3,000 mi]. Nereid orbits Neptune every 360 days, following an elliptical path. Nereid has a diameter of about 241 km [150 mi].

Neptune was mathematically predicted to exist before its discovery. Neptune was found in 1846. *See also* PLANET.   J.M.C./C.R.

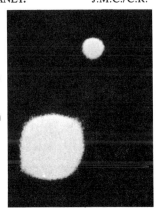

Neptune has two satellites. The larger is Triton, the white mass in the upper part of this photograph. The planet Neptune cannot be seen by the unaided eye.

NEPTUNIUM (nep tü′ nē əm) Neptunium (Np) is a radioactive metallic element. Its atomic number is 93 and its atomic weight is 237.05. Neptunium melts at 640°C [1,184°F] and boils at 3,902°C [7,056°F]. Its relative density is 20.3.

Neptunium occurs in nature only in very small amounts. It was first made in 1940 by two American physicists, Edwin Macmillan and Philip Abelson. They bombarded the element uranium with particles called neutrons.

Neptunium has 13 isotopes. (*See* ISOTOPE.) The longest-lived isotope is neptunium-237. This isotope decays by half in 2,200,000 years. Neptunium-237 is used in instruments for detecting neutrons. *See also* RADIOACTIVITY; TRANSURANIC ELEMENT.

M.E./J.R.W.

NERVE CELL (nərv′ sel) A nerve cell is a cell that carries messages. The messages are in the form of electric signals, or nerve impulses. They travel through the cell and are passed on to other cells. Millions and millions of nerve cells linked together make up the nervous system. (*See* NERVOUS SYSTEM.) The brain itself contains about ten thousand million nerve cells. With the spinal cord and nerves throughout the body, all made of nerve cells, it forms a vast communications network.

A shorter term for nerve cell is neuron. There are many different sizes and shapes of neurons. However, they have the same basic plan. There is a cell body. This is wider than the other parts of the cell. It contains the nucleus, which is the neuron's control center for growth and other activities. From the cell body, numerous branches spread out and meet the branches of other cells. The shorter branches are called dendrites. They carry messages inward, toward the cell body. The longest branch is called the axon. It carries messages away from the cell body. In some neurons the axon is only a fraction of a millimeter long. In others it may be a meter or more long. The main nerves of the body are bundles of axons.

Nerve impulses are picked up by dendrites from other neurons or from sensory cells. (*See* SENSES.) They travel through the cell body, and then out through the axon. From the axon the impulses are passed on to another neuron or to an effector cell. The effector cell may be a muscle cell or a gland cell that responds to the impulses.

The branches of a neuron do not quite touch the other cells they meet. There is a tiny gap between them, called a synapse. Nerve impulses have to jump across a synapse to reach another cell.

A nerve impulse is a wave of electrical and chemical activity. It spreads through the thin membrane at the surface of the cell. There is normally a difference of electric charge between the inside and the outside of the membrane. This is because there are more potassium ions inside and more sodium ions outside. They do not balance. The cell uses chemical energy to "pump" ions through the membrane. This produces an electric charge. (*See* IONS AND IONIZATION.)

When a part of the membrane is stimulated, the arrangement of the molecules of the membrane is changed and ions can pass through. Potassium ions rush out, and sodium ions rush in. This means that the electric charge of the membrane disappears. When this happens, it upsets the arrangement of molecules in the membrane nearby. It, in turn, also allows ions to pass through. In this way, the activity spreads in a wave along the nerve cell.

When the impulse reaches a synapse, it causes the release of a chemical into the tiny gap. The chemical passes across the gap and alters the molecules in the membrane of the next cell. The impulse starts again, and travels onwards.

Nerve impulses travel at different speeds in different kinds of nerves. Fat neurons con-duct signals very quickly, up to 100 meters per second. In fine neurons, the impulse may only move 5 meters a second. The nerves through which impulses travel fastest have membranes coated with a sheath of a fatty substance called myelin.

Unlike most other cells in the body, nerve cells cannot be replaced when they die or are accidentally destroyed. This is why injury to the brain, or interruption of its blood supply, is so dangerous. D.M.H.W./J.J.F.

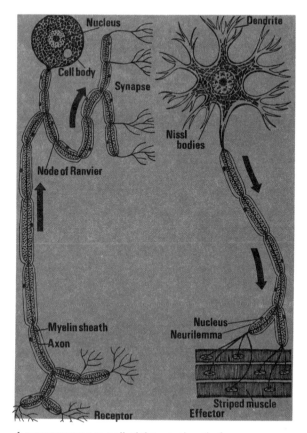

A sensory nerve cell picks up signals from a receptor. The signal passes to the spinal cord, and a synapse occurs with a motor nerve cell. The signal passes to muscle fibers, and they contract.